# SHOP TOO

A basic guide showing the right tool for each type of job and its proper use

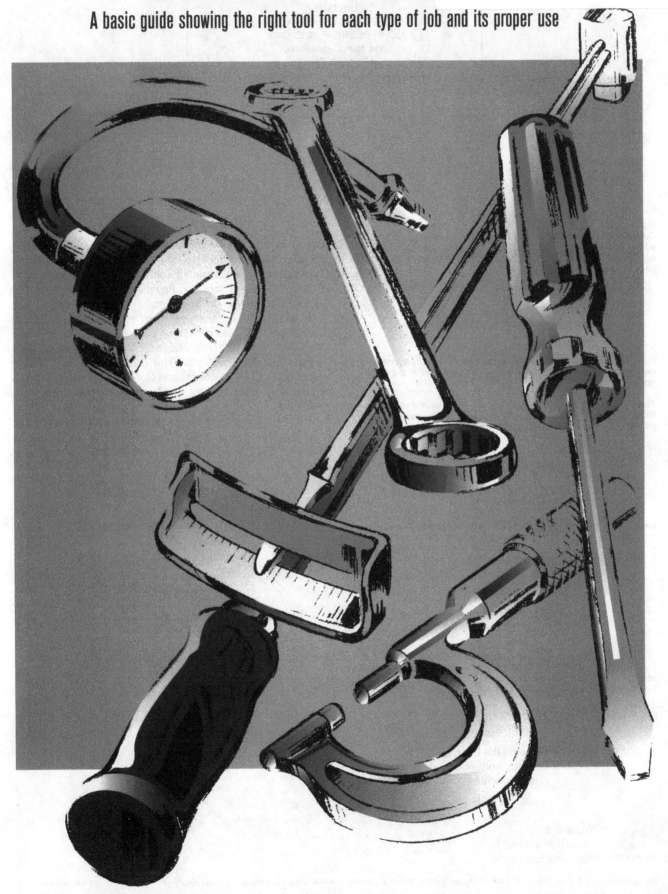

# FUNDAMENTALS OF SERVICE

**PUBLISHER**
DEERE & COMPANY
JOHN DEERE PUBLISHING
one John Deere Place
Moline, IL 61265
http://www.johndeere.com/publications
1–800–522–7448

Fundamentals of Service (FOS) is a series of manuals created by Deere & Company. Each book in the series is conceived, researched, outlined, edited, and published by Deere & Company, John Deere Publishing. Authors are selected to provide a basic technical manuscript that could be edited and rewritten by staff editors.

HOW TO USE THE MANUAL: This manual can be used by anyone — experienced mechanics, shop trainees, vocational students, and lay readers.

Persons not familiar with the topics discussed in this book should begin with Chapter 1 and then study the chapters in sequence. The experienced person can find what is needed on the "Contents" page.

Each guide was written by Deere & Company, John Deere Publishing staff in cooperation with the technical writers, illustrators, and editors at Almon, Inc. — a full-service technical publications company headquartered in Waukesha, Wisconsin (www.almoninc.com).

FOR MORE INFORMATION: This book is one of many books published on agricultural and related subjects. For more information or to request a FREE CATALOG, call 1–800–522–7448 or send your request to address above or:

ACKNOWLEDGEMENTS:

John Deere gratefully acknowledges help from the following groups: Owatonna Tool Co., Armstrong-Bray and Co., Chek-Chart Corp., The Cincinnati Tool Co., The Cleveland Twist Drill Co., Crescent Tool Co., Fayette R. Plumb, Inc., General Motors Corp., Heinrich Tools, Inc., The Lufkin Rule Co., Lutz File and Tool Co., Mathias Klein and Sons, Inc., Marsh Instrument Co., Morgan Vise Co., Nuday Co., Peterson Manufacturing Co., The Ridge Tool Co., Snap-On Tools Corp., The Stanley Works, The L.S. Starrett Co., Sterling Products Co., J. H. Williams and Co. We also wish to thank a host of John Deere people who helped with this project.

**Visit Us on the Internet**
**http://www.johndeere.com/**
**publications**

We have a
long-range interest in
JOHN DEERE    Vocational Education

# CONTENTS

## SHOP TOOLS

## APPENDIX

## ANSWERS TO TEST YOURSELF QUESTIONS

## INDEX

# SHOP TOOLS

Fig. 1 — Tools Don't Make the Service Technician — But They Help

## Introduction

Tools don't make the service technician — but they help. Knowing how to use and care for them will put you a step ahead of the crowd.

To get the best out of your tools, follow these three rules:

1. Purchase only quality tools.

2. Keep tools in good condition.

3. Use the right tool for the job.

Service technicians are known by the tools they use, so buy the best, keep them in good shape, and use them right.

In this book, we'll cover the following tools:

- Screwdrivers
- Hammers
- Pliers
- Wrenches
- Chisels
- Punches
- Files
- Hacksaws
- Vises

- Clamps
- Twist Drills
- Taps and Dies
- Screw Extractors
- Pullers
- Pick-Up Tools
- Inspection Mirrors
- Tubing Cutters
- Soldering Equipment
- Feeler Gauges
- Micrometers
- Dial Indicators
- Spring Testers
- Pressure Gauges
- Compression Testers
- Speed-Measuring Tools

# Screwdrivers

Screwdrivers are the tools most easily misused. Regardless of other abilities, screwdrivers should only be used to install and remove threaded fasteners.

Screwdrivers discussed here are divided into eight designs:

- Common
- Phillips®
- Clutch-Head
- Offset
- Starting
- Pozidriv® or Supadriv®
- Torx®
- Scrulox® (Square Tip)

Each one allows you to produce a twisting motion to tighten or loosen screws — but for different jobs.

Keep screwdrivers organized to make selection easy. Keep handles clean and free of grease and oil that could cause slippage. Discard screwdrivers with broken or damaged handles.

## COMMON SCREWDRIVER

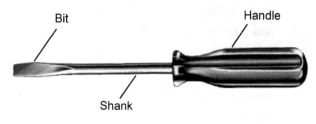

Bit

Handle

Shank

JDPX3020

*Fig. 2 — Common Screwdriver*

Never use a screwdriver (Fig. 2) as a cold chisel, a punch, or a prying bar. If you must tap on the screwdriver, use one made for tapping.

Don't twist the shank of a standard screwdriver with a pliers or wrench. If necessary, use a heavy-duty screwdriver with a square shank.

Never use a screwdriver to check an electrical circuit.

Don't hold work in the hand while using a screwdriver — the point may slip and hurt you. A good rule is never to get any part of your body in front of the screwdriver bit.

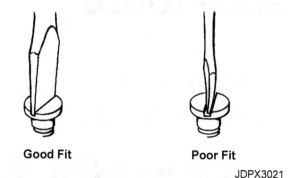

Good Fit          Poor Fit

JDPX3021

*Fig. 3 — Be Sure the Screwdriver Fits the Screw Slot*

Be sure the screwdriver bit is wide enough and fills the slot in the screw head (Fig. 3). Too small a bit will twist and damage the screw.

Always hold the screwdriver shank vertical to the screw head as you twist it.

If the screwdriver bit becomes rounded or broken, it can be reground as shown:

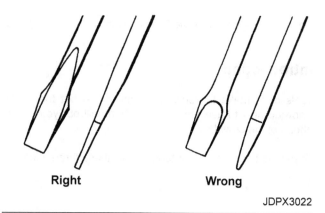

Right          Wrong

JDPX3022

*Fig. 4 — Grinding the Screwdriver Blade*

1. Grind the tip until it is straight and at right angles to the shank (Fig. 4). The sides should have very little taper and should never come to a sharp point at the tip.

2. **IMPORTANT: Never hold the screwdriver against the grinding wheel for a long time.** Dip the bit in water to keep it cool. This will prevent loss of tempering and softening of the bit.

3. If the bit is correctly ground, it will stay down in the screw slot regardless of the twisting force. If ground with too much taper, the bit will rise out of the slot as it is turned.

*NOTE: Only the end of the screwdriver bit is hardened, so there is a limit to how many times it can be successfully reground.*

## PHILLIPS SCREWDRIVER

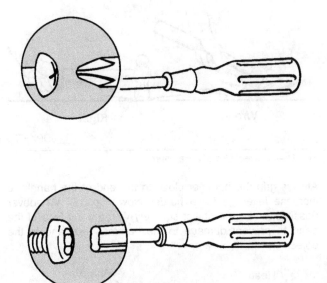

JDPX3023

*Fig. 5 — Phillips and Clutch-Head Screwdrivers*

This screwdriver (Fig. 5) has a cross-shaped, pointed tip. It will not slip sideways out of the cross slots of a cross-recessed head screw, but more force must be exerted in keeping it in the slots.

If the bit is damaged, it is not practical to repair it.

## CLUTCH-HEAD SCREWDRIVER

This screwdriver (Fig. 5) is used with screws for sheet metal and trim where a neat appearance is vital. This type of screw is sometimes called a figure-eight or butterfly screw. The tip of the screwdriver is very strong and stays in the screw opening with only moderate pressure.

## OFFSET SCREWDRIVER

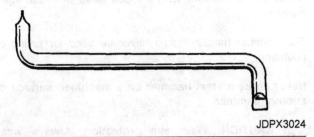

JDPX3024

*Fig. 6 — Offset Screwdriver*

Offset screwdrivers (Fig. 6) are used where space is limited and the screw is hard to reach. Bits are usually at right angles to each other, allowing the screw to be turned a quarter turn at a time by using opposite ends alternately.

Use the offset screwdriver cautiously as the bit has a tendency to ride out of the slot and damage the screw head.

## STARTING SCREWDRIVER

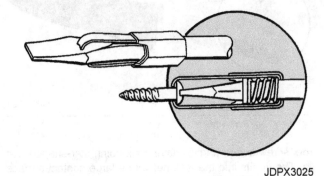

JDPX3025

*Fig. 7 — Starting Screwdriver (Shown Holding Screw)*

Starting screwdrivers (Fig. 7) are used for removing and installing screws in places difficult to reach by hand. Once a screw is started, a common screwdriver can often be used to finish the job.

Other starting screwdrivers have twisting centers or are magnetized to hold the screws.

## POZIDRIV OR SUPADRIV SCREWDRIVER

JDPX3026

*Fig. 8 — Pozidriv or Supadriv Screwdriver*

This screwdriver (Fig. 8) is similar to the Phillips screwdriver, but the screwdrivers should never be interchanged with each other. Misuse can cause tool and fastener damage.

The driving surface in the Pozidriv fastener is flat; a Phillips fastener driving surface is angled. This makes for a tighter, more positive fit between tip and fastener.

## TORX SCREWDRIVER

JDPX3027

*Fig. 9 — Torx Screwdriver*

Torx screwdrivers (Fig. 9) have a six-point, star-shaped, flat tip. The tip fits into the fastener with a large contact surface engagement. This allows for higher torques to be applied to the fastener without damaging the fastener. Tip sizes are designated by a number preceded by the letter "T".

## SCRULOX (SQUARE TIP) SCREWDRIVER

JDPX3028

*Fig. 10 — Scrulox (Square Tip) Screwdriver*

The square tip screwdriver is used to install and remove scrulox fasteners. These types of fasteners are used primarily in recreational vehicles and truck body panels.

## Hammers

After screwdrivers, hammers can be the next most abused tool. There is a right way and a wrong way to use a hammer, regardless of type.

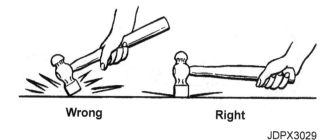

**Wrong**          **Right**

JDPX3029

*Fig. 11 — Correct Use of a Hammer*

Always grip the hammer close to the end of the handle to increase leverage for a harder blow (Fig. 11). Whenever possible, strike the object squarely with the full face of the head to prevent damage to the hammer face and to the object.

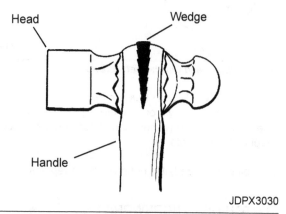

JDPX3030

*Fig. 12 — Correct Installation of Hammer Head on Handle*

The handle of a steel hammer extends through the head and is held tightly in the head by a wedge (Fig. 12) or an epoxy bond. If the wedge starts to come out, drive it in again to tighten the handle. If the wedge is lost, replace it before using the hammer. If the epoxy bond is loose or broken, replace the hammer.

**Never use a hammer with a loose head or a damaged handle.**

The hammer handle should never be used for prying or pounding.

**Never strike a steel hammer on a machined surface or another hammer.**

 **CAUTION: Wear eye protection. Always wear goggles when striking hardened tools and hardened metal surfaces. This will protect your eyes from flying chips. Whenever possible, use soft-faced hammers (plastic, wood, or rawhide) when striking hardened surfaces.**

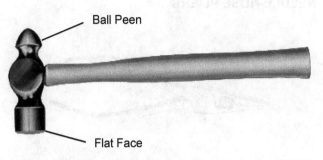

Fig. 13 — Ball Peen Hammer

JDPX3031

Ball peen hammers (Fig. 13) are most commonly used by shop service technicians. The flat face is for hammering, and the ball face is for rounding off rivets and similar jobs.

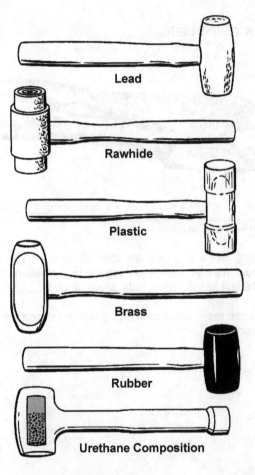

Fig. 14 — Soft Hammers

JDPX3032

Soft hammers (Fig. 14) are used in place of steel hammers to protect machined surfaces or fragile parts. These hammers are commonly made of lead, rawhide, plastic, brass, rubber, or urethane material. Urethane hammers are sometimes filled with lead shot to produce a "dead blow."

## Pliers

### COMBINATION PLIERS

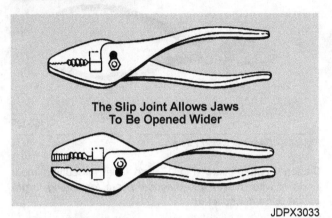

**The Slip Joint Allows Jaws To Be Opened Wider**

JDPX3033

Fig. 15 — Combination Pliers

Combination pliers (Fig. 15) are often misused. They are made for *holding work* — not for tightening or loosening nuts.

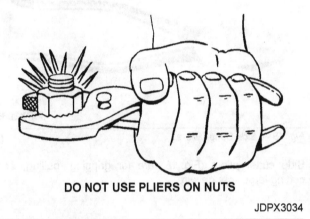

**DO NOT USE PLIERS ON NUTS**

JDPX3034

Fig. 16 — Wrong Use of Pliers

A slip joint permits the jaws to be opened wider. For extra-wide objects, rib-joint pliers are used.

**Avoid using pliers on hardened surfaces as this dulls the teeth of the pliers and they lose their grip.**

## DIAGONAL CUTTER PLIERS

JDPX3035

*Fig. 17 — Diagonal Cutter Pliers*

Diagonal cutter pliers (Fig. 17) are ideal for cutting most kinds of wire. *Never use diagonal pliers for cutting large-gauge or hardened wire.*

## SIDE CUTTER PLIERS

JDPX3035

*Fig. 18 — Side Cutter Pliers*

Side cutter pliers (Fig. 18) are for gripping, pulling, and cutting larger-gauge wire.

## NEEDLE-NOSE PLIERS

JDPX3035

*Fig. 19 — Needle-Nose Pliers*

Needle-nose pliers (Fig. 19) are used primarily for handling small objects and for reaching into restricting areas. Never force them beyond their gripping capacity.

## LOCK-GRIP PLIERS

JDPX3035

*Fig. 20 — Lock-Grip Pliers*

Lock-grip pliers (Fig. 20) are specially designed to clamp and hold material. One jaw is adjustable to fit different sizes of nuts, bolt heads, pipes, rods, sheet, or plate.

Never use these pliers on material where marring the finish is a problem.

## SNAP RING PLIERS

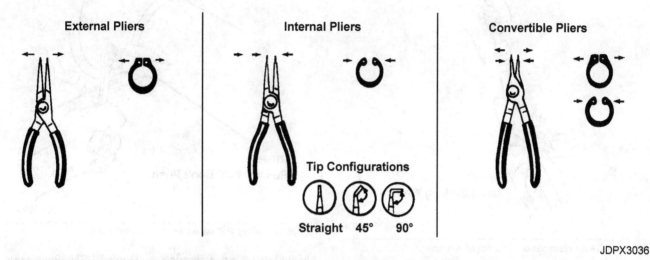

Fig. 21 — External, Internal, and Convertible Snap Ring Pliers

Snap ring pliers (Fig. 21) are used to spread or compress snap rings as they are removed or installed.

Angled tips are available for hard-to-reach snap rings. This is a handy tool and helps prevent over-expanding of snap rings.

Fig. 22 — Use of Snap Ring Pliers

## OTHER TYPES OF PLIERS

Special types of pliers are also available for certain jobs: battery (terminal nut) pliers, water pump nut pliers, ignition pliers, hose clamp pliers, brake spring pliers, retaining ring pliers (Fig. 22), groove-grip snap ring pliers, horseshoe lock ring pliers, and slip-joint (channel) pliers.

## CARE OF PLIERS

Keep pliers clean and occasionally put a drop of oil on the joint pin. This will prevent rust and lubricate the joint.

## Wrenches

There are many types of wrenches available, each intended for a specific use. In this book, we will discuss the following most common wrenches:

- Open-End
- Adjustable Open-End
- Box
- Flarenut/Line
- Socket
- Hex Key
- Spanner
- Torque

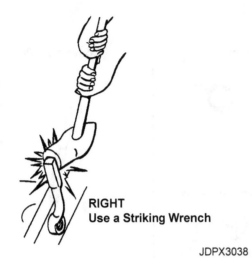

**RIGHT**
**Use a Striking Wrench**

JDPX3038

*Fig. 23 — Never Hammer on a Standard Wrench*

*Never hammer on a standard wrench.* Use a heavy-duty striking wrench designed for use with a hammer (Fig. 23).

**WRONG**
**Never Use a Bar or Pipe on a Wrench**

JDPX3039

*Fig. 24 — Never Use a Bar or Pipe on a Wrench*

*Never use a bar or pipe to increase leverage on a wrench* (Fig. 24). The only exception is when the work is hard to reach and you must use an extension, as with a socket wrench (Fig. 34).

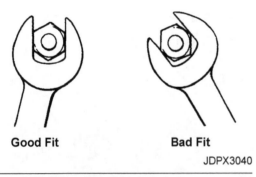

**Good Fit**          **Bad Fit**

JDPX3040

*Fig. 25 — Correct Fit of Wrench on Nut Is Important*

*Be sure the wrench correctly fits the nut or bolt head* (Fig. 25).

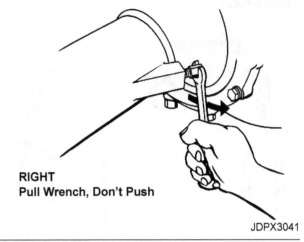

**RIGHT**
**Pull Wrench, Don't Push**

JDPX3041

*Fig. 26 — Always Pull on a Wrench — Don't Push*

**Always PULL on a wrench — Don't PUSH.** Save your knuckles (Fig. 26). If you must push, use the base of your palm and keep your hand open.

## OPEN-END WRENCHES

Open-end wrenches have an opening at each end. The openings designate the size of wrench in inches (or millimeters) and are often combined, as 5/16 by 3/8 (metric wrenches — 8 mm by 10 mm). These figures refer to the distance across the flats of the nut or bolt and not the bolt diameter.

JDPX3042

*Fig. 27 — Loosen Nuts in Crowded Places by "Flopping" the Wrench*

The head and opening of an open-end wrench is normally at an angle of 15 or 22-1/2 degrees to the body (Fig. 27).

The offset angle allows you more swing space in crowded places by "flopping" the wrench as shown.

## ADJUSTABLE OPEN-END WRENCHES

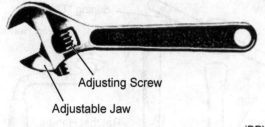

Adjusting Screw

Adjustable Jaw

JDPX3043

*Fig. 28 — Adjustable Open-End Wrench*

The adjustable open-end wrench (Fig. 28) has a sliding jaw moved by an adjusting screw. This wrench is not meant to take the place of an open-end wrench, except when an odd-sized nut or bolt is encountered. This does help to cut down the number of open-end wrenches you need to carry.

Adjustable wrenches aren't intended for hard service — treat them gently.

Remember these three points:

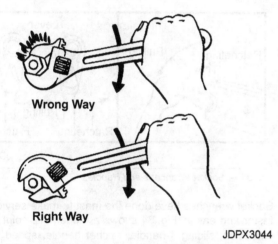

**Wrong Way**

**Right Way**

JDPX3044

*Fig. 29 — Correct Use of Adjustable Open-End Wrench (Tightening Shown)*

1. Always place the adjustable wrench on the nut so that the pulling force is applied to the stationary jaw side of the wrench (Fig. 29). This side can withstand much greater force.

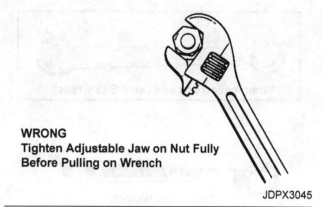

**WRONG**
**Tighten Adjustable Jaw on Nut Fully**
**Before Pulling on Wrench**

JDPX3045

*Fig. 30 — Tighten the Adjustable Wrench on the Nut*

2. After placing the wrench on the nut, tighten the adjusting screw so that the wrench fits the nut snugly (Fig. 30). Otherwise the nuts will be rounded off.

3. Keep the wrench clean. Wash it occasionally in cleaning solvent, and apply a light oil to the adjusting screw and slide.

## BOX WRENCHES

Box wrenches completely surround the nut to avoid slipping and are handy for working in close quarters.

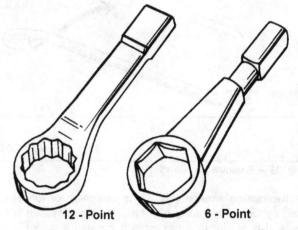

**12 - Point**          **6 - Point**

JDPX3046

*Fig. 31 — Striking Box Wrenches*

In place of the hexagonal or six-sided opening, most box wrenches have 12 notches arranged in a circle and are called 12-point wrenches (Fig. 31). A 12-point wrench can be used to continuously loosen or tighten a nut with a minimum swing of the handle of only 15 degrees, compared to a 30- or 60-degree swing of the open-end wrench. Larger box wrenches are also available in 6-point styles. A 6-point wrench should be used on higher torqued hardware to provide greater contact, reducing possible damage to hardware or tool.

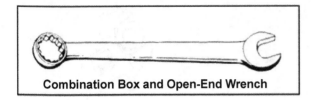

**Combination Box and Open-End Wrench**

**Offset Box Wrench**

JDPX3047

*Fig. 32 — Box Wrenches*

Combination box and open-end wrenches (Fig. 32) can speed up nut-and-bolt installations. The box end is used to break loose or snug down the nut, while the open end is used for greater speed the rest of the time.

Some box wrenches are made with an offset at one or both ends (Fig. 32). This provides clearance for your hands and saves knuckles.

## FLARENUT/LINE WRENCHES

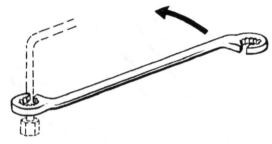

JDPX3048

*Fig. 33 — Flarenut/Line Wrench*

A flarenut/line wrench (Fig. 33) is designed for loosening and tightening hydraulic, A/C, fuel, and brake system fitting nuts. It is similar to a box wrench but has a cutout large enough to slip over the tubing and maintain maximum contact with fitting nuts so that they are not damaged when loosened and tightened. When using the wrench, pull only in the direction of the arrow in Fig. 33 to avoid spreading the wrench opening.

## SOCKET WRENCHES

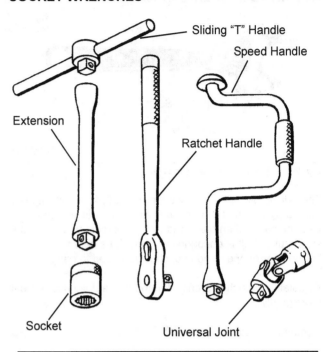

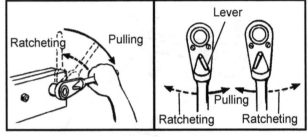

JDPX3049

*Fig. 34 — Socket Wrenches and Handles*

Socket wrenches have done the most to make service work faster and easier. Fig. 34 shows a modern 12-point socket, extension, sliding T-handle, ratchet handle, speed handle, and universal joint. In addition, several extensions and L-handles are available. Combined in various ways, these socket sets can do many nut-and-bolt jobs. Larger sockets are also available in 6-point styles.

To use the socket wrench with a ratchet, you select the size of socket that fits the nut, engage it on the ratchet handle, and place the socket on the nut.

Inside the head of the ratchet handle is a pawl or dog, which engages or fits into one or more of the ratchet teeth. Pulling on the handle in one direction, the dog holds in the ratchet teeth and turns the socket. Moving the handle in the other direction, the dog ratchets over the teeth, permitting the handle to be backed up without moving the socket (see insert in Fig. 34). That's why the ratchet handle can be worked so rapidly — the socket does not have to raised off the nut to get another "bite." The handle ratchets in one direction when tightening a nut and in the other direction when loosening a nut.

A means usually is provided on the handle for changing the direction of ratcheting (see insert in Fig. 34). On some makes there is a little lever that is flipped to the right to make the head ratchet when the handle is moved in a counterclockwise direction. This is the way you want it to work when tightening a nut. When unscrewing a nut, the lever is flipped to the left and the handle then ratchets in a clockwise direction.

The reason that a modern socket wrench set is so adaptable for repair work is that, in addition to the set of sockets and the ratchet handle, it contains numerous other accessories.

A hinged offset handle accessory is very convenient. To loosen a tight nut, the handle can be swung so as to be at a right angle to the socket and thus provide the greatest possible leverage. Then, after the nut is loosened to the point where it turns easily, the handle can be hinged into the vertical position and twisted by the fingers to quickly remove the nut from the bolt or the stud.

Another part of the socket set is the sliding offset handle. The head can be positioned at the end or at the center of the handle. The sliding offset and an extension bar can be made up as a "T" handle.

Speed handles sometimes called "speeders" or "spinners" are convenient for many jobs such as removing or tightening oil pan screws. The speed handle is worked like a brace that the woodworker uses with a bit to bore holes. A speed handle will help you get cylinder head nuts off in a hurry after they are first broken loose with the sliding offset or the ratchet handle.

A universal joint frequently comes in very handy when working on nuts in places where a straight wrench cannot be used. The universal joint enables you to work the wrench handle at an angle with the socket. Often this is a big help when working in close places.

Large socket wrench sets also contain extra-deep sockets for use on spark plugs and on nuts that are a long way down on the bolts, such as on U-bolts.

Another accessory to the socket wrench set is a handle that measures the amount of pull you put on the wrench. This is called a "torque wrench." We will discuss torque wrenches later.

Keep all parts of the socket set free of dirt and grit. Wash them occasionally in cleaning solvent and apply a light oil to all universal joints and ratchets.

Never use hand sockets or adapters on electric or air powered tools; use only impact sockets and adapters for power tools. Most sockets can be distinguished by finish; hand sockets are chrome plated and impact sockets are black oxide finish.

## HEX KEY WRENCHES

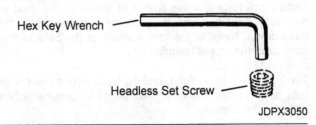

Fig. 35 — Hex Key Wrench

Hex key wrenches (Fig. 35) have a hexagonal cross-section. They are used for hardware with hexagonal recesses such as headless set screws, socket head cap screws, and button head cap screws. Most are L-shaped bars of tool steel, though T-handle, long-reach, and bit applications are also available.

## SPANNER WRENCHES

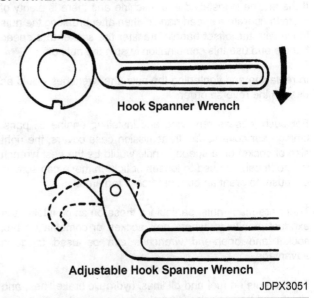

Fig. 36 — Spanner Wrenches

Spanner wrenches (Fig. 36) are usually special tools supplied with a machine. There are a number of types: the hook type (shown), U-shaped hook type, end spanner, pin spanner, and face pin spanner.

## WHICH WRENCH TO USE?

Now that we have talked about all of the ordinary wrenches used by service technicians, you may wonder how you are to find out which is the best type of wrench to use for the particular work you are doing. Should it be an open-end wrench, an adjustable wrench, a socket wrench, a box wrench, or a combination box and open-end wrench? This is something that is best learned by actual experience, but there are a few simple rules that will be helpful.

First, determine if the fastener Is unified inch or metric size. Unified inch fasteners use dashes or marks on the head or nut. Metric fasteners have the property class number on the head or nut. Refer to the torque tables at the back of this manual for the proper identification.

The type of job to be done, and the location and number of nuts or cap screws are the next things to consider when selecting the wrench.

Usually, if there are a number of nuts to be taken off or put on, the socket wrench set is what you should use. In removing the cylinder head from an engine, for example, you would first break the nuts loose by using a socket on a hinged offset handle with the handle bent over at an angle of practically 90 degrees to provide the necessary leverage. Then after the nuts were broken loose, the hinged handle would be held in the vertical position and twisted with the fingers to run them off.

If the engine is installed in a machine and there is plenty of room to operate a speed handle, then after breaking the nuts loose with the offset handle, transfer the socket to a speed handle and use this combination to spin the nuts off.

In replacing and tightening the nuts, the wrenches would be used in the reverse order.

For such jobs as removing and installing engine oil pans, timing gear covers, and transmission case covers, the right size of socket on a speed handle would be the best wrench to use. It can be used to loosen or tighten these cap screws because no great amount of force is required.

There are many nuts, particularly those on some intake and exhaust manifolds, where box, socket, or combination box socket and open-end wrenches can be used to good advantage.

For the nuts on fuel and oil lines, hydraulic brake lines, and clutch and transmission control rods, open-end wrenches or flarenut/line wrenches are the only wrenches that can be used.

With a little actual experience in the shop, and after using each type of wrench in the tool kit a few times, you will find that with a little THINKING it is not at all difficult to select the type best suited for the job and to pick the right-size wrench. A good service technician is someone who can use the head as well as the hands — who can coordinate the brain and the muscles.

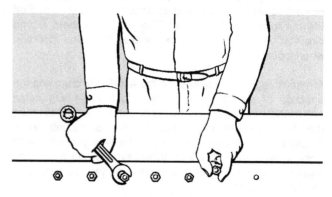

JDPX3052

*Fig. 37 — Using Both Hands to Get the Job Done in Half the Time*

For instance, in replacing a series of nuts and bolts, you will find you can get the job done in about half the time if you use both hands simultaneously instead of just one (Fig. 37). It is something like learning to use a typewriter – the beginner starts with two fingers but the experienced typist uses all ten. It is just a matter of practice.

## TORQUE WRENCHES

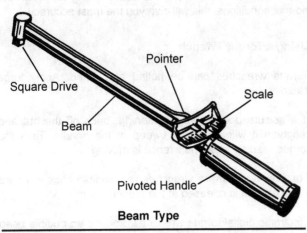

**Beam Type**

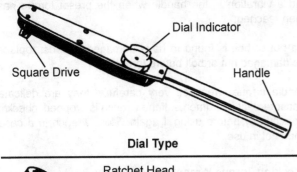

**Dial Type**

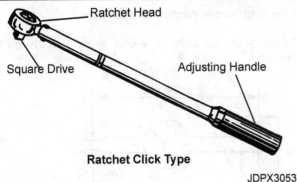

**Ratchet Click Type**

JDPX3053

*Fig. 38 — Torque Wrenches*

A torque wrench (Fig. 38) measures resistance to turning — called **torque**.

Torque and tension are not the same thing. **Torque** is **twist**, measured in foot-pounds (Newton-meters). **Tension** is a straight **pull**, measured in pounds (Newtons). Wrenches designed to measure the tightness of a bolt or nut are **torque** wrenches, not tension wrenches.

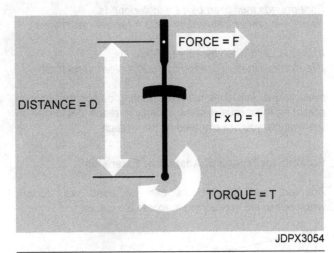

*Fig. 39 — Formula for Torque*

TORQUE is based on the fundamental law of the lever — FORCE x DISTANCE = TORQUE. This is shown in Fig. 39.

Lever length is the distance from the center of the drive square (Fig. 38) to the axis of the handle pivot where the force is concentrated.

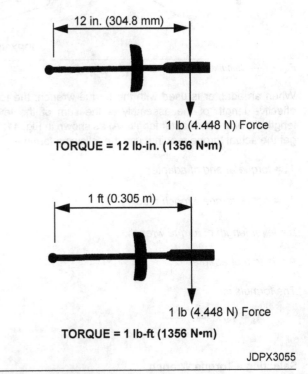

*Fig. 40 — Units for Measuring Torque*

If the lever length is measured in inches (millimeters) and the force in pounds (Newtons), then the torque developed is measured in **inch-pounds (Newton-millimeters)**. If the lever length is measured in feet (meters), then the result is termed **foot-pounds (Newton-meters)** (Fig. 40).

*Foot-pounds multiplied by 12 = inch-pounds.*
*(Newton-meters multiplied by 1000 = Newton-millimeters)*

*Inch-pounds divided by 12 = foot-pounds.*
*(Newton-millimeters divided by 1000 = Newton-meters)*

Most torque wrenches have a signaling device that can be preset for the torque desired. When you reach that torque on the wrench, you are signaled by the wrench.

### Formula for Torque of Adapter or Extension

Adapters and attachments can be used with torque wrenches to aid in reaching inaccessible places.

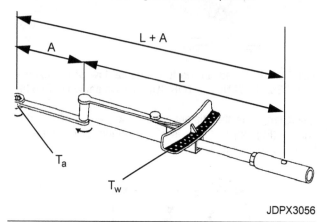

JDPX3056

*Fig. 41 — Calculating Torque with an Adapter*

When an adapter is used with the torque wrench, the total effective length of the assembly is the sum of the lever length (L) plus the adapter length (A) as shown in Fig. 41. To get the actual torque reading, use the following formula:

$T_a$ = torque at end of adapter

$T_w$ = actual torque wrench reading

$L$ = lever length of torque wrench

$A$ = length of adapter

*The formula is:*

$$T_a = T_w \times \frac{L + A}{L}$$

### Selecting a Torque Wrench

Selecting the proper size and range of torque wrench is important in getting accurate results. A good rule of thumb is to select a torque wrench having enough capacity so that your working range is within the middle two quarters of the scale.

For example, if you choose a 600 foot-pound (814 N•m) capacity torque wrench, any job within 150 to 450 foot-pound (203 to 610 N•m) is the best working range. Under normal conditions, this will give you the most accuracy.

### Using a Torque Wrench

Torque wrenches can be pulled or pushed. Apply force steadily.

If a seizure occurs while tightening, back off the nut and retighten it with a steady sweep of the handle. Take the torque reading while the wrench is moving.

For click-type torque wrenches, an audible click is heard when tension is released at the preset torque.

Electronic digital torque wrenches produce an audible beep and a vibration in the handle when the preset torque has been reached.

If a nut or bolt is found to have damaged threads, replace the damaged nut or bolt before torquing.

Handle torque wrenches very carefully, they are delicate measurement instruments. If the wrench is dropped, check it for accuracy before using it again. Store wrench in a case when not in use.

### Checking Torque Wrench for Accuracy

To check the accuracy of a rigid torque wrench, do the following:

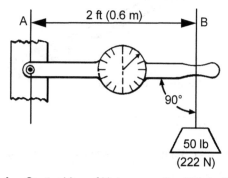

A = Center Line of Nut     B = Point of Suspension

JDPX3057

*Fig. 42 — Checking Torque Wrench for Accuracy*

1. Hang the torque wrench on a fixed nut as shown in Fig. 42.

2. Set the indicator to "0." (This will compensate for the weight of the wrench.)

3. Hang a known weight from the wrench handle at any known distance from the center of the nut as shown.

4. Weight in pounds multiplied by the distance from A to B in feet will give you the lb-ft (N•m) of torque. This figure should agree with the indicator reading.

Example shown: 50 lbs x 2 ft = 100 lb-ft
(22.7 kg x 9.81 = 222 N;
222 N x 0.6 m = 133 N•m)
Note: 9.81 is a factor for gravitational pull.

Remember that any weight or distance can be substituted in the formula, Weight x Distance = Torque.

*NOTE: To check the accuracy of flexible torque wrenches, hang the weight from the pivot point of the handle. Weight x Distance will then give you the Torque.*

Always check wrenches within the range where they are normally used.

### Why Proper Torque Is All-Important

Bolt torque is based on this concept: For a bolt to stay tightened, it must be tightened enough so that the load *in the bolt* is greater than the loads that the bolt must *absorb* during operation.

*Over-tightened* bolts are "stretched" until their threads are damaged or assembly parts are warped or misaligned.

*Under-tightened* bolts allow a "shearing" force to develop between the mating parts as they try to move. If the parts impose a greater stress than the stress or load in the bolt, they will eventually fatigue and break the bolt or work it loose. Shear bolts are designed to fail under predetermined loads. Always replace shear bolts with identical grade bolts.

Up to 90 percent of applied torque is used for overcoming friction, but the percent varies with different types of bolts and nuts. Other variables include the material in the parts to be held together, location of the assembly, forces exerted on it, and lubrication of the bolt threads. In short, every torquing job varies, and that is why a specific torque is given in the machine technical manual for each location.

A general guide for torquing various types of bolts and nuts is given in the tables at the back of this manual.

## TORQUE ANGLE GAUGE

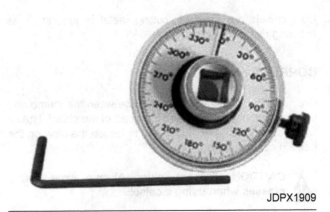

JDPX1909

*Fig. 43 — Torque Angle Gauge*

The torque angle gauge (Fig. 43) is required to properly tighten torque-to-yield bolts as used on aluminium cylinder heads etc., on many late model engines.

Torque-to-yield bolt tightening specifications require the bolt to be torqued to specification and then turned an additional specified angle.

## TORQUE MULTIPLIER

*Fig. 44 — Torque Mulitplier*

The torque mulitplier (Fig. 44) is used to loosen and tighten threaded fasteners where high torques are required. As a torque multiplier it is able to generate thousands of foot-pounds with precision and ease.

The 4:1 torque multiplication is achieved by a planetary gear train design. Multipliers can be stacked to provide high mechanical ratios.

# Chisels

Cold chisels are used for cutting metal in jobs such as breaking rivets and splitting nuts.

## CORRECT USAGE

Ordinarily the chisel should be held between the thumb and first finger about an inch from the head of the chisel. Hold it with a steady but rather loose grip to lessen the blow on the hand in case of a miss.

 **CAUTION: Prevent injury. Always wear safety glasses when using a chisel.**

A chisel will cut any metal softer than itself. Always use a chisel that is big enough for the job and a hammer that is heavy enough for the size of the chisel; the larger the chisel, the heavier the hammer.

## FLAT COLD CHISEL

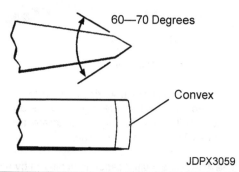

JDPX3058

*Fig. 45 — Flat Cold Chisel*

60—70 Degrees

Convex

JDPX3059

*Fig. 46 — Correct Shape of Flat Cold Chisel Edge*

The flat cold chisel (Fig. 45) is the one most commonly used. The cutting edge is slightly convex (curved outward) as shown in Fig. 46. This causes the center portion to receive the greatest shock, thus protecting the weaker corners. Cutting edge angle should be 60 to 70 degrees for general use.

## SPECIAL COLD CHISELS

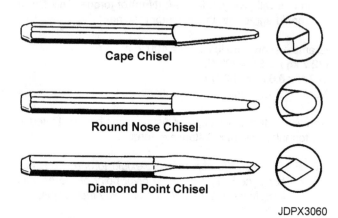

Cape Chisel

Round Nose Chisel

Diamond Point Chisel

JDPX3060

*Fig. 47 — Special Chisels*

**Cape chisels** (Fig. 47) are used for cutting keyways, narrow grooves, and square corners.

**Round nose chisels** (Fig. 47) are used for cutting semicircular grooves and chipping inside corners that have a fillet or radius.

**Diamond point chisels** (Fig. 47) are used for cutting V-grooves and square corners.

## PROPER CARE OF CHISELS

IMPORTANT: **When grinding a chisel, never hold it against the grinding wheel for any great length of time. Dip it frequently in water or coolant to keep it cool. Unless this is done, heat caused by friction with the grinding wheel will draw the temper and cause the cutting edge to become soft and almost useless.**

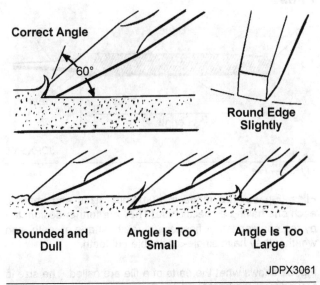

Correct Angle

60°

Round Edge Slightly

Rounded and Dull

Angle Is Too Small

Angle Is Too Large

JDPX3061

*Fig. 48 — Results of Correct and Incorrect Chisel Grinding*

Fig. 48 shows the results of correct and incorrect chisel grinding.

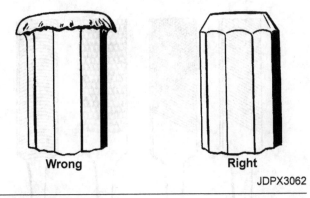

Wrong

Right

JDPX3062

*Fig. 49 — Chisel Heads*

The head of a chisel will spread out or "mushroom" after being used a great deal as shown in Fig. 49. This spreading is rough, and will injure the inside of the hand if the chisel should slip. Also, pieces may break away from the overhang with enough force to cause injury. For safety, keep the chisel head ground down as shown in Fig. 49.

# Punches

## CORRECT USAGE

When using a punch, hold it with a steady, but rather loose grip to lessen the blow on the hand in case of a miss. Always use a hammer proportionately large enough for the punch.

 **CAUTION: Always wear safety glasses when using a punch or drift.**

Use the proper size punch for the job and a proper size hammer for the size of the punch. The larger the punch, the heavier the hammer.

## PROPER CARE OF PUNCHES

The head of a punch will, in time, spread, or "mushroom" like that of a chisel and should be ground down to prevent injury. Refer to Fig. 49.

The tip of a starting punch, pin punch and brass drift can also mushroom or become chewed and gouged, resulting in a rounded or uneven tip that could be potentially dangerous. Any mushrooming should be ground off and the tip end ground flat and perpendicular to the centerline of the punch.

As with chisels, care should be taken when grinding the tip of a punch. Never overheat the tip; dip it frequently in water or coolant to keep it cool.

## STARTING PUNCH

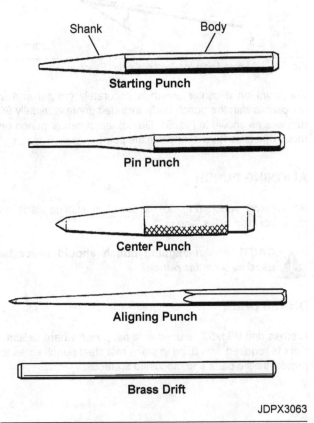

Shank

Body

Starting Punch

Pin Punch

Center Punch

Aligning Punch

Brass Drift

JDPX3063

*Fig. 50 — Punches*

A starting punch (Fig. 50) has a long gentle taper that extends from the tip to the body of the punch. This type of punch is used to knock out rivets and to start driving out straight or tapered pins.

## PIN PUNCH

A pin or drift punch (Fig. 50) is used for driving out pins after the starting punch can no longer be used.

 **CAUTION: Never use a pin punch to start a pin. Since it has a slim shank, a hard blow may cause it to break or bend.**

## CENTER PUNCH

A center punch (Fig. 50) is used to mark the location of a hole that is to be drilled and to eliminate drill "wandering."

Frequently, a center punch is used for marking the relationship between mating parts.

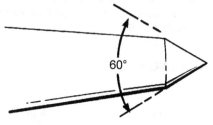

JDPX3064

Fig. 51 — Correct Angle for Point of Center Punch

The point on a center punch is accurately ground and is concentric with the punch body. Included angle is usually 60 degrees as shown in Fig. 51. Do not use a center punch on metal that is so hard it may dull the point.

## ALIGNING PUNCH

An aligning punch (Fig. 50) is useful in shifting parts so corresponding holes "line up."

 **CAUTION: An aligning punch should never be used as a center punch.**

## BRASS DRIFT

A brass drift (Fig. 50) is used as a pin punch where delicate work is required. It is used in place of a steel punch so as to protect fragile parts and machined surfaces.

## Files

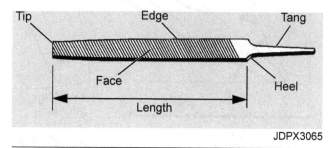

JDPX3065

Fig. 52 — File

Files (Fig. 52) are made in numerous sizes and shapes, each one having a specific use. They are further designated by the coarseness or fineness of teeth, shape of teeth, and whether they have single- or double-cut teeth.

Fig. 52 shows what the parts of a file are called. The size is figured from the heel to end of tip.

There are many kinds of files, but here we will cover only those a service technician will normally use.

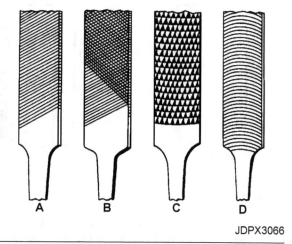

JDPX3066

Fig. 53 — Four Types of File Teeth

Shown in Fig. 53 are four representative files generally used in shops.

"A" shows a **mill file**, which received its name by having been used to sharpen saws. Mill files are always single-cut, meaning only one row of teeth appears on the blade.

"B" illustrates a **machinist's file**, which has double-cut teeth.

"C" is a **rasp cut file** on which all teeth have been individually cut and disconnected from each other for independent teeth in cutting.

"D" is a **curved tooth file,** which has a single row of teeth cut on the blade in a curve to aid in self-cleaning.

Mill and machinist's files are further classified with reference to coarseness of teeth into *bastard*, *second-cut*, and *smooth-cut*.

Mill files are generally used for tool sharpening. Machinist's files are used for filing and finishing machine parts. Rasp files are used for cutting wood and very soft metals. The curved tooth file is used on aluminum and steel sheets.

## CORRECT USE OF FILES

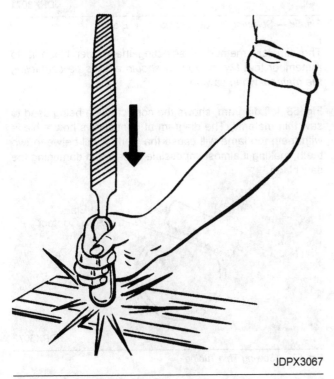

JDPX3067

*Fig. 54 — Tightening File Handle*

Before attempting to use any file, equip it with a tight-fitting handle similar to that shown in Fig. 54. This eliminates the danger of injuring your hand.

Normally *PUSH the file across the work, cutting only on the forward stroke*. To prevent damage to teeth, raise the file from the work on the return stroke.

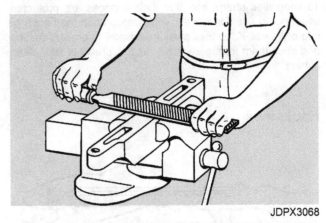

JDPX3068

*Fig. 55 — Correct Method of Draw-Filing*

When it becomes necessary to finish a flat surface, for example a gasket surface, it should be draw-filed. This is done by using a machinist's file and drawing the file crosswise over the work with a light pressure (Fig. 55). Holding the file in this manner allows it to cut when moving in both directions.

When using a file, *apply only enough pressure to keep the file cutting.*

Never hammer on a file, or use it for prying. After the teeth have become clogged, do not use the file until it has been properly cleaned. Learn to tap the file at the end of the stroke to clear the teeth of chips.

## PROPER CARE OF FILES

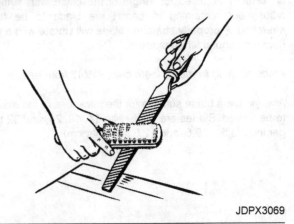

JDPX3069

*Fig. 56 — File Card*

Clean a file by using a file card (Fig. 56). This is a brush with short, stiff wire bristles. If chips are left after using the file card, they should be lifted out with a pointed or flattened cleaning wire called a "scorer," which is included as a part of most file cards.

To keep files sharp, see that their surfaces are protected when not in use. Do not throw files around on the bench or into a drawer. Keep files away from water to prevent rusting and keep them from getting oily, as this prevents fast, clean cutting.

## Hacksaws

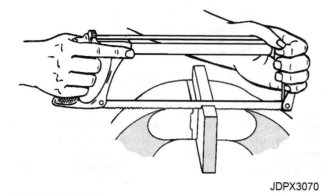

JDPX3070

*Fig. 57 — Correct Way to Use a Hacksaw*

Hacksaw (Fig. 57) frames are designed to take blades of various lengths. The blade can be positioned at various angles along its axis.

### CORRECT USE OF HACKSAW

When placing a blade in a hacksaw frame, be sure the frame is correctly adjusted for length of the blade with sufficient adjustment remaining to permit the blade to be *tightly stretched*. A properly stretched blade will vibrate with a clear humming sound when plucked.

*Place blade in frame so teeth point AWAY from handle.*

Always use a blade suitable for the thickness of the material to be sawed. Blades are made with 14, 18, 24, and 32 teeth per inch (5.5, 7. 9.5, and 12.5 teeth per cm).

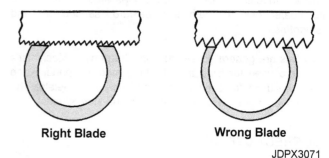

| Right Blade | Wrong Blade |

JDPX3071

*Fig. 58 — Selecting the Correct Hacksaw Blade*

The simplest method of selecting the proper blade is to remember that *two saw teeth should always be contacting the material when sawing.*

Fig. 58, left diagram, shows the correct blade being used to saw thin material, The diagram at right shows how a blade with teeth too large will cause the work to fall between two teeth, making it almost impossible to saw and damaging the saw blade.

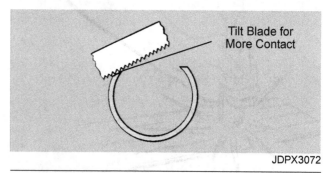

Tilt Blade for More Contact

JDPX3072

*Fig. 59 — Sawing Thin Tubing*

When cutting very thin material, such as tubing, shift the angle of the saw blade as cutting progresses to increase the area of contact between blade and material, allowing as many teeth as possible to contact the work at one time (Fig. 59).

Use sufficient pressure on the forward or cutting stroke so that the teeth actually bite into metal. It is not necessary to lift the blade from the work on the back stroke, but pressure should be relieved. Always use sufficient pressure to keep the blade from getting pinched or jammed in the work as this often breaks teeth or blade.

Except when starting, use the full length of the blade on every stroke.

For efficient cutting of average metal, work the blade at 40 to 50 strokes a minute. Reduce this rate for harder metals. There is a limit to the hardness of metal that can be sawed.

## PROPER CARE OF HACKSAWS

Wipe the blade occasionally with an oily cloth to keep it from rusting. Also, keep the blade away from other tools to eliminate the possibility of teeth being broken or dulled.

Normally, metal hacksaw blades are never sharpened due to the fine teeth and the hardness of the metal. For these reasons, replace them when worn.

## Vises

A vise is a heavy-duty holding tool. Several types are generally used in the shop.

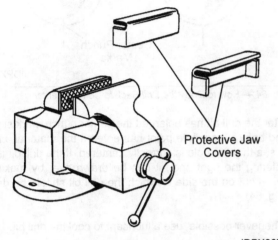

Protective Jaw Covers

JDPX3073

*Fig. 60 — Machinist's Bench Vise*

Fig. 58 shows the most commonly used machinist's **bench vise**. Also illustrated are jaw covers of soft metal used to hold machined parts to prevent marring the surfaces. A similar type is the **anvil vise**. Light hammering may be done on the stationary jaw of this vise.

JDPX3074

*Fig. 61 — Drill Press Vise*

Fig. 61 shows a **drill press vise**, which should always be used when drilling parts at a drill press. It is dangerous to attempt to drill parts when holding them with pliers or hands.

## CORRECT USE OF VISES

Never use a hammer to tighten or loosen a vise; hand pressure is sufficient.

Always use a vise big enough for the parts or type of work to be held.

When round parts must be held, soft metal or hard wood jaws can be used to prevent slipping or damage to parts. Whenever finished surfaces must be held, be sure to use soft metal jaw covers as shown in Fig. 60 to prevent marring the finish.

## Clamps

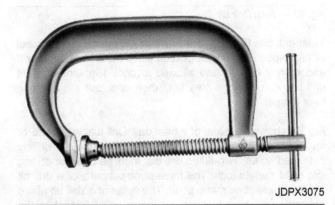

JDPX3075

*Fig. 62 — C-Clamp*

C-clamps (Fig. 62) are more portable and versatile than vises, but do not hold the complete work stationary. However, they are handy for fastening materials together, as while welding.

## Twist Drills

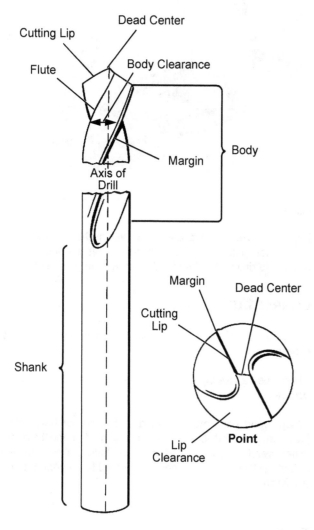

JDPX3076

*Fig. 63 — Twist Drill Bit*

Twist drill bits (Fig. 63) are made of either carbon tool steel or high-speed tool steel. Carbon steel will lose its temper if excessively heated and allowed to cool. High-speed steel drill bits can become "red hot," then cool, but still not lose their temper.

Fig. 63 shows the parts of a twist drill. Drill bits with three or four flutes are used only for enlarging drilled holes or drilling out cored holes. Two-fluted drill bits must be used for drilling into solid metal stock. The three principal parts of a drill bit are the shank, body, and point. The flutes of a drill bit afford channels for chips to pass out, carry any lubricant to the point, and provide correct rake to the lips, thereby causing chips to curl tightly to occupy less space.

## CORRECT USE OF DRILLS

When using a low-speed, slow-feed method of drilling, carbon tool steel drill bits can be used.

When high-speed or fast-feed of the drill bit is necessary, use drill bits of high-speed tool steel.

Always center punch the exact spot to drill holes accurately.

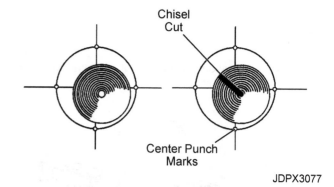

JDPX3077

*Fig. 64 — How to Draw the Drill Back to Correct Center*

After the drill bit has enlarged the center punch mark slightly and before the whole point has entered the material, check to see that the hole is correctly centered. If the drill bit is not entering the right spot, it can be drawn over by making a chisel cut on the side to which the drill bit should be drawn (Fig. 64).

Whenever possible, use a lubricant to cool the drill bit.

### Grinding or Sharpening Drill Bits

Before using a drill bit, be sure it is sharp and ground according to the material to be drilled.

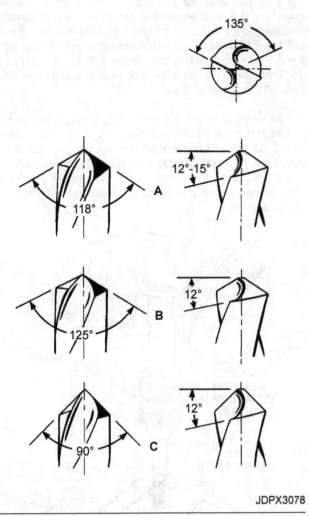

Fig. 65 — *Common Shape of Drill Bits*

Several attachments for grinders are available for grinding drills accurately.

*NOTE: Always be sure to keep drill bits cool while grinding by dipping them occasionally in suitable coolant — water or oil.*

## Taps and Dies

### TAPS

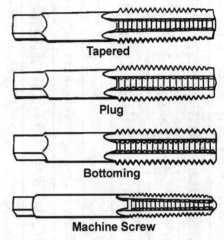

Fig. 66 — *Four Kinds of Taps*

Fig. 65 illustrates the most commonly used shapes. The *lips* do the cutting and therefore must be ground to a sharp edge. These lips or cutting edges must be of uniform length.

The portion behind the lips is ground down on an angle to provide lip clearance (see Fig. 65, right column).

For steel and cast iron, these lips are ground on a 59° angle to the drill axis or 118° included angle as shown in Fig. 65. Note that lip clearance angle on "A" is 12° to 15°.

"B" illustrates a drill bit ground to drill heat-treated steels and drop forgings, Note that the included angle is greater and lip clearance angle is 12°.

When drilling softer material such as wood, hard rubber, fiber, or soft cast iron, a much smaller included angle can be used as shown in "C."

When any unusual material such as spring steel must be drilled, consult a machinist's handbook to obtain the correct angles and shapes.

Taps are used for cutting internal threads. There are many styles of taps, but for general shop use, a set of taper, plug, bottom, and machine screw taps should be provided (Fig. 66).

Each type of tap will have to be provided in both National Fine (N.F.) and National Coarse (N.C.) threads, as well as in the various sizes: 1/4, 5/16, etc.

Metric taps are provided in various sizes with the dimension for pitch (distance between threads) also listed. The metric pitch is listed in place of N.C. or N.F.

The *taper tap* is used to tap completely through the hole. Notice that it has a long gradual taper that allows the tap to start easily.

The *plug tap* is used to tap threads partway through. The *bottoming tap* is used to cut threads all the way to the bottom of a blind hole. The plug tap should be used in the blind hole before the bottoming tap, as the bottoming tap will not start well.

The plug tap is the most widely used and, except when running threads completely to the bottom of a blind hole, will work satisfactorily.

The *machine screw tap* handles the small diameter, fine thread jobs.

## USING THE TAP

### TAP DRILL SIZES
Recommended for
AMERICAN NATIONAL SCREW THREAD PITCHES

**COARSE STANDARD THREAD (N. C.)** Formerly U. S. Standard Thread

| Sizes | Threads Per Inch | Outside Diameter at Screw | Tap Drill Sizes | Decimal Equivalent of Drill |
|---|---|---|---|---|
| 1 | 64 | .073 | 53 | 0.0595 |
| 2 | 56 | .086 | 50 | 0.0700 |
| 3 | 48 | .099 | 47 | 0.0785 |
| 4 | 40 | .112 | 43 | 0.0890 |
| 5 | 40 | .125 | 38 | 0.1015 |
| 6 | 32 | .138 | 36 | 0.1065 |
| 8 | 32 | .164 | 29 | 0.1360 |
| 10 | 24 | .190 | 25 | 0.1495 |
| 12 | 24 | .216 | 16 | 0.1770 |
| 1/4 | 20 | .250 | 7 | 0.2010 |
| 5/16 | 18 | .3125 | F | 0.2570 |
| 3/8 | 16 | .375 | 5/16 | 0.3125 |
| 7/16 | 14 | .4375 | U | 0.3680 |
| 1/2 | 13 | .500 | 27/64 | 0.4219 |
| 9/16 | 12 | .5625 | 31/64 | 0.4843 |
| 5/8 | 11 | .625 | 17/32 | 0.5312 |
| 3/4 | 10 | .750 | 21/32 | 0.6562 |
| 7/8 | 9 | .875 | 49/64 | 0.7656 |
| 1 | 8 | 1.000 | 7/8 | 0.875 |
| 1 1/8 | 7 | 1.125 | 63/64 | 0.9843 |
| 1 1/4 | 7 | 1.250 | 1 7/64 | 1.1093 |

**SPECIAL THREAD (N. S.)**

| Sizes | Threads Per Inch | Outside Diameter at Screw | Tap Drill Sizes | Decimal Equivalent of Drill |
|---|---|---|---|---|
| 1 | 56 | .0730 | 54 | 0.0550 |
| 4 | 32 | .1120 | 45 | 0.0820 |
| 4 | 36 | .1120 | 44 | 0.0860 |
| 6 | 36 | .1380 | 34 | 0.1110 |
| 8 | 40 | .1640 | 28 | 0.1405 |
| 10 | 30 | .1900 | 22 | 0.1570 |
| 12 | 32 | .2160 | 13 | 0.1850 |
| 14 | 20 | .2420 | 10 | 0.1935 |
| 14 | 24 | .2420 | 7 | 0.2010 |
| 1/4 | 64 | .0625 | 3/64 | 0.0469 |
| 3/32 | 48 | .0938 | 49 | 0.0730 |
| 1/8 | 40 | .1250 | 38 | 0.1015 |
| 5/32 | 32 | .1563 | 1/8 | 0.1250 |
| 5/32 | 36 | .1563 | 30 | 0.1285 |
| 3/16 | 24 | .1875 | 26 | 0.1470 |
| 3/16 | 32 | .1875 | 22 | 0.1570 |
| 7/32 | 24 | .2188 | 16 | 0.1770 |
| 7/32 | 32 | .2188 | 12 | 0.1890 |
| 1/4 | 24 | .250 | 4 | 0.2090 |
| 1/4 | 27 | .250 | 3 | 0.2130 |
| 1/4 | 32 | .250 | 7/32 | 0.2187 |
| 5/16 | 20 | .3125 | 17/64 | 0.2656 |
| 5/16 | 27 | .3125 | J | 0.2770 |
| 3/8 | 32 | .3125 | 9/32 | 0.2812 |
| 3/8 | 20 | .375 | 21/64 | 0.3281 |
| 3/8 | 27 | .375 | R | 0.3390 |
| 7/16 | 24 | .4375 | X | 0.3970 |
| 7/16 | 27 | .4375 | Y | 0.4040 |
| 1/2 | 12 | .500 | 27/64 | 0.4219 |
| 1/2 | 24 | .500 | 29/64 | 0.4531 |
| 1/2 | 27 | .500 | 15/32 | 0.4687 |
| 9/16 | 27 | .5625 | 17/32 | 0.5312 |
| 5/8 | 12 | .625 | 35/64 | 0.5469 |
| 5/8 | 27 | .625 | 19/32 | 0.5937 |
| 11/16 | 11 | .6875 | 19/32 | 0.5937 |
| 11/16 | 16 | .6875 | 5/8 | 0.6250 |
| 3/4 | 12 | .750 | 43/64 | 0.6719 |
| 3/4 | 27 | .750 | 23/32 | 0.7187 |
| 7/8 | 12 | .875 | 51/64 | 0.7969 |
| 7/8 | 18 | .875 | 53/64 | 0.8281 |
| 7/8 | 27 | .875 | 27/32 | 0.8437 |
| 1 | 12 | 1.000 | 59/64 | 0.9219 |
| 1 | 27 | 1.000 | 31/32 | 0.9687 |

**FINE STANDARD THREAD (N. F.)** Formerly S.A.E. Thread

| Sizes | Threads Per Inch | Outside Diameter at Screw | Tap Drill Sizes | Decimal Equivalent of Drill |
|---|---|---|---|---|
| 0 | 80 | .060 | 3/64 | 0.0469 |
| 1 | 72 | .073 | 53 | 0.0595 |
| 2 | 64 | .086 | 50 | 0.0700 |
| 3 | 56 | .099 | 45 | 0.0820 |
| 4 | 48 | .112 | 42 | 0.0935 |
| 5 | 44 | .125 | 37 | 0.1040 |
| 6 | 40 | .138 | 33 | 0.1130 |
| 8 | 36 | .164 | 29 | 0.1360 |
| 10 | 32 | .190 | 21 | 0.1590 |
| 12 | 28 | .216 | 14 | 0.1820 |
| 1/4 | 28 | .250 | 3 | 0.2130 |
| 5/16 | 24 | .3125 | I | 0.2720 |
| 3/8 | 24 | .375 | Q | 0.3320 |
| 7/16 | 20 | .4375 | 25/64 | 0.3906 |
| 1/2 | 20 | .500 | 29/64 | 0.4531 |
| 9/16 | 18 | .5625 | 0.5062 | 0.5062 |
| 5/8 | 18 | .625 | 0.5687 | 0.5687 |
| 3/4 | 16 | .750 | 11/16 | 0.6875 |
| 7/8 | 14 | .875 | 0.8020 | 0.8020 |
| 1 | 14 | 1.000 | 0.9274 | 0.9274 |
| 1 1/8 | 12 | 1.125 | 1 3/64 | 1.0468 |
| 1 1/4 | 12 | 1.250 | 1 11/64 | 1.1718 |

### TAP DRILL SIZES (METRIC)

| Bolt Diameter (in mm) | Distance Between Threads (in mm) | Diameter of Drill (in mm) | Bolt Diameter (in mm) | Distance Between Threads (in mm) | Diameter of Drill (in mm) |
|---|---|---|---|---|---|
| M 2 | 0.4 | 1.6 | M 22 | 2.5 | 19.5 |
| M 2.2 | 0.45 | 1.75 | M 24 | 3 | 21 |
| M 2.5 | 0.45 | 2.05 | M 27 | 3 | 24 |
| | | | M 30 | 3.5 | 26.5 |
| M 3 | 0.5 | 2.5 | | | |
| M 3.5 | 0.6 | 2.9 | M 33 | 3.5 | 29.5 |
| M 4 | 0.7 | 3.3 | M 36 | 4 | 32 |
| M 4.5 | 0.75 | 3.7 | M 39 | 4 | 35 |
| | | | M 42 | 4.5 | 37.5 |
| M 5 | 0.8 | 4.2 | | | |
| M 6 | 1 | 5 | M 45 | 4.5 | 40.5 |
| M 8 | 1.25 | 6.8 | M 48 | 5 | 43 |
| M 10 | 1.5 | 8.5 | M 52 | 5 | 47 |
| M 12 | 1.75 | 10.2 | M 56 | 5.5 | 50.5 |
| M 14 | 2 | 12 | M 60 | 5.5 | 55 |
| M 16 | 2 | 14 | M 64 | 6 | 58 |
| M 18 | 2.5 | 15.5 | M 68 | 6 | 62 |
| M 20 | 2.5 | 17.5 | | | |

JDPX3080

Fig. 67 — Tap Drill Size Charts

After determining the diameter, and number of threads per inch (pitch for metric) of the screw or stud that will enter the tapped hole, use a tap drill size chart to find what size hole to drill. See Fig. 67 as a sample chart.

For example, suppose you find that you want a threaded hole for a 3/8 stud with coarse (National Coarse) threads. Referring to the top chart in Fig. 67, you will find the 3/8 N.C. will have 16 threads per inch. Looking directly across from the 3/8 size, you will find that the tap drill size is listed as 5/16. This means that for a 3/8 N.C. stud, you must first drill a hole 5/16 in diameter.

For an example of using a metric tap, suppose you want a threaded hole for an M5 stud. Referring to the bottom chart in Fig. 62, you will find the M5 size will have a pitch of 0.8 mm. Looking directly across from the M5 size, you will find that the tap drill size is listed as 4.2. This means that for an M5 stud with a pitch of 0.8 mm, you must first drill a hole 4.2 mm in diameter.

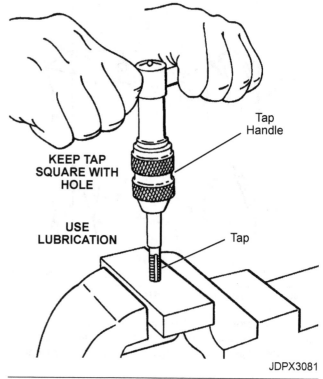

KEEP TAP SQUARE WITH HOLE

USE LUBRICATION

Tap Handle

Tap

JDPX3081

Fig. 68 — Using the Tap to Thread a Drilled Hole

If the hole is to be tapped partway through, use the proper size plug tap. Place the tap in a tap handle, and carefully start the tap in the hole (Fig. 68). Place some tap lubricant on the tap. After threading the tap in one or two turns, back the tap up about a quarter to one-half turn to break the chip. Repeat this process as your tapping continues.

Be careful that the hole does not clog with chips. It may be necessary to withdraw the tap and remove the chips. Taps are quite brittle. Use them with care, and make certain you use the proper size tap drill.

## DIES

Dies are used to cut external threads. A die of the correct size is placed in a diestock (handle) and it is turned. Use lubricant, back up every one or two turns, and keep free of chips.

Dies are often adjustable in size so you can enlarge or reduce (slightly) the outside diameter of a threaded area.

Both taps and dies should be cleaned, slightly oiled, and placed in a protective box for storage.

## SPECIAL TAPS AND DIES

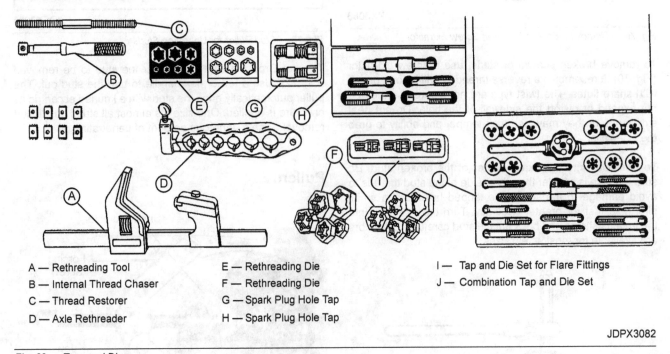

A — Rethreading Tool
B — Internal Thread Chaser
C — Thread Restorer
D — Axle Rethreader

E — Rethreading Die
F — Rethreading Die
G — Spark Plug Hole Tap
H — Spark Plug Hole Tap

I — Tap and Die Set for Flare Fittings
J — Combination Tap and Die Set

JDPX3082

*Fig. 69 — Taps and Dies*

The service technician will also find use for a few special taps and dies as illustrated in Fig. 69.

One form of rethreading tool is shown in (A). It is placed on the thread and turned.

(B) shows an internal thread chaser used to clean up dirty or damaged internal threads.

The thread restorer, (C), is handy for quickly reconditioning external threads.

The axle rethreader, (D), is placed around the good thread area, clamped shut, and is then turned back over the damaged area.

Nut or rethreading dies, (E and F), can be turned on a damaged thread. An ordinary box wrench can be used to turn them.

(G and H) show spark plug hole taps. These are very handy to clean up damaged or carboned plug hole threads.

A combination tap and die set for tube flare fittings is illustrated in (I).

A combination tap and die set is pictured in (J).

## Screw Extractors

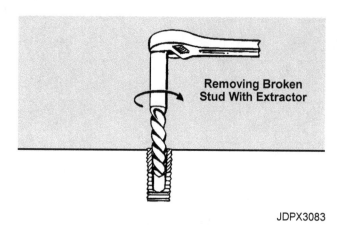

JDPX3083

*Fig. 70 — Removing Broken Stud with Screw Extractor*

To remove broken screws or studs, use a screw extractor (Fig. 70). It resembles a reverse-threaded drill bit or a punch with sharp flutes. The twist type are not tapered so they do not expand or distort the sidewall of the hole. Do not heat extractors, or they may lose their temper and ability to grab the sidewalls.

**To use:** Drill into the **exact center** of the broken stud. Be sure the hole is smaller than the inside of the stud threads to avoid damage to threads in the tapped hole. Drill a small pilot hole first for greater accuracy. Turn the extractor into the hole as shown and back out the stud carefully. Extractors are available for most screw sizes.

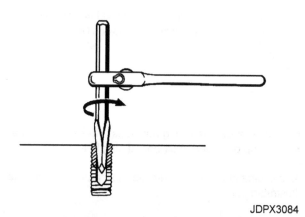

JDPX3084

*Fig. 71 — Using Chisel as Emergency Stud Remover*

In an emergency, a diamond-point chisel can be used to remove a broken stud (Fig. 71). Simply drive the chisel into the stud after drilling a small hole into the center of the stud. Then turn the chisel carefully with a wrench.

To remove unbroken studs, use a stud puller.

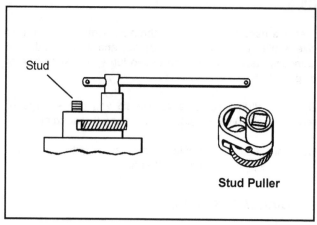

JDPX3085

*Fig. 72 — Stud Puller for Unbroken Studs*

**To use:** Drop the stud puller over the stud to be removed (Fig. 72). Use a tee or flex handle to turn the stud out. The puller automatically grips the stud with a knurled eccentric as pressure is applied. One size fits almost all studs. In all stud removals, use a generous amount of penetrating oil.

## Pullers

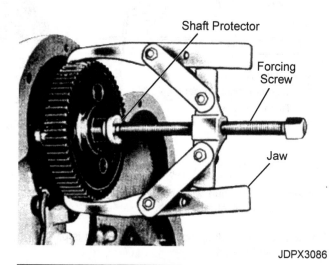

JDPX3086

*Fig. 73 — Gear Puller*

Fitted parts can be damaged during removal and installation unless care is taken. Using hammers, pry bars, and chains may only cause more problems. However, special pullers that fit the parts and apply force evenly and smoothly are often the answer (Fig. 73).

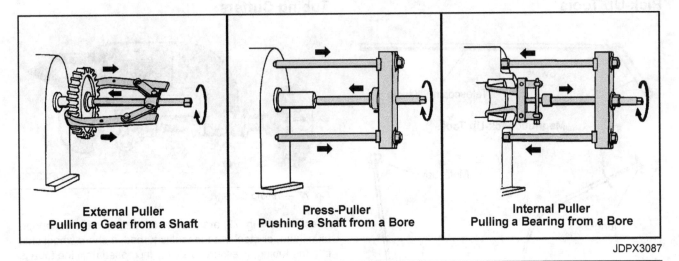

| External Puller Pulling a Gear from a Shaft | Press-Puller Pushing a Shaft from a Bore | Internal Puller Pulling a Bearing from a Bore |

JDPX3087

Fig. 74 — Pullers – Three Basic Types

There are three types of pullers (Fig. 74):

- External Puller
- Press-Puller
- Internal Puller

EXTERNAL pullers grip the back of the object with their jaws as shown while the forcing screw pushes against the stationary part, such as a shaft. When the forcing screw is turned, the jaws pull the object.

PRESS-pullers have legs that mount on the stationary part while the object is pushed or pressed. As the forcing screw is turned into the object, the object is removed.

INTERNAL pullers also have legs that mount on the stationary part while the forcing screw pulls the object. However, the jaws go *inside* the object and reach out to grip it. This puller is commonly used to pull a bearing from a bearing bore as shown.

RULES FOR USE OF PULLERS

1. Don't use a hammer — use a puller. Machined parts and precision bearings that are pressed on can be ruined by forcing them.

2. Don't use a pry bar — use a puller. A puller gives a smooth, even pull and prevents "cocking" the part you are pulling.

3. Choose the right type and size of puller for each job, The main questions are: Can you reach it? Can you grip it? Do you have enough power? This leads you automatically to the type of puller you should use.

4. For special pulling jobs, use a combination puller; for bigger jobs, use a hydraulic puller.

5. Don't overload a puller. A general rule is to use a puller with a forcing screw that is at least one-half the diameter of the shaft.

6. Place a shaft protector over the end of a shaft before installing a puller against the shaft (see Fig. 73).

7. When installing parts that must be forced into place, normally use a shop press rather than trying to use a puller.

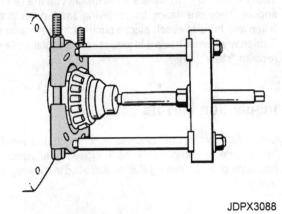

JDPX3088

Fig. 75 — Using Knife-Edge Pulling Attachment

When a bearing must be pulled from a shaft, but the bearing is against a flat housing, use a knife-edge pulling attachment (Fig. 75). This prevents pulling only on the outer race of the bearing and ruining it.

## Pick-Up Tools

**Magnetic Pick-Up Tool**

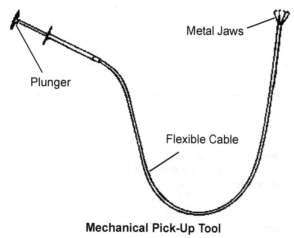

**Mechanical Pick-Up Tool**

JDPX3089

*Fig. 76 — Pick-Up Tools*

These tools (Fig. 76) have a small magnet on the tip or metal fingers. They are handy for retrieving small parts that have fallen into hard-to-reach places such as transmission cases. This may prevent having to disassemble a complete unit to recover "stray" parts.

## Inspection Mirrors

Inspection mirrors are handy for reaching in and viewing the "blind" side of components, as in closed gear cases. A pin flashlight or a "trouble light" is an extra aid in viewing with the mirror.

## Tubing Cutters

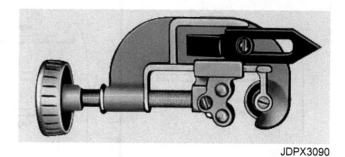

JDPX3090

*Fig. 77 — Tubing Cutter*

These tools (Fig. 77) are used to cut tubing made of copper, aluminum, or steel. As the tool is turned, a sharp wheel cuts into the tubing. Pressure is slowly increased until the tube is cut off cleanly.

The tubing cutter is sometimes sold in a kit that includes a cutter, a tube flaring tool, and a tube bending tool.

## Soldering Equipment

Soldering is the process of joining two pieces of metal by using a third metal as an adhesive. Unlike welding, soldering does not involve melting the two metals being joined; only the joining metal is melted. Standard solder melts at 800°F (426°C), far below the melting point of most metals.

*NOTE: Welding is covered in a separate FOS manual, FOS-52B, on "Welding."*

Most metals can be soldered. The only exceptions are chromium, beryllium, manganese-bronze, and titanium.

There are three methods of soldering:

1. Soldering iron

2. Torch

3. Resistance

In the SOLDERING IRON method, the iron is heated either electrically or in a flame periodically.

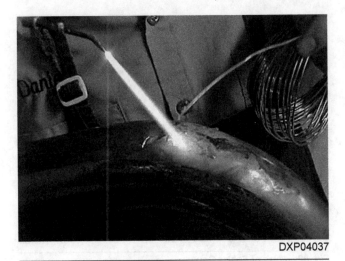

Fig. 78 — Soldering with a Torch

Soldering with a TORCH (Fig. 78) is faster because it produces more heat. Torches are used for soldering heavy sheet metal, pipes, and heavy tubing that require more heat than soldering irons can produce.

RESISTANCE soldering is similar to resistance (spot) welding except that the metals are not melted. Heat created by an electrical current is applied across the joint until the metals are hot enough to melt solder. The solder flows into the joints and the heat is then removed.

## SOLDERING MATERIAL

Solder is a mixture of tin and lead — usually equal parts of each. "Hard solder," which melts at a higher temperature, may contain twice as much tin as lead.

Solder is available in stick and in wire rolls. Some types contain their own flux, while others must be dipped in flux or have flux applied to the joint areas. (Flux is a substance such as borax or rosin, which helps to fuse the two metals together.)

## HOW TO SOLDER

1.  Clean the joint thoroughly.

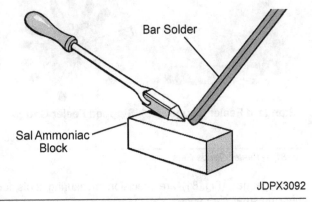

Fig. 79 — Tinning the Soldering Iron

2.  Tin the soldering iron by rubbing it on a sal ammoniac block, then touching solder to it (Fig. 79). Or simply heat the soldering iron and touch the solder to it.

3.  Heat both pieces to be soldered and apply flux (if flux is not included in the solder).

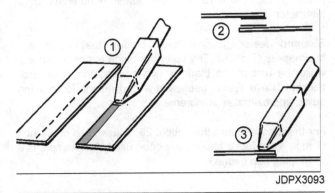

Fig. 80 — Soldering a Lap Joint

4.  Apply solder to the joints – not to the iron (1) (Fig. 80).

5.  Lap the two pieces (2) and hold the heated iron over the seam (3) to fuse the solder. Remove heat after the solder has thoroughly penetrated the joint.

6.  Hold the two lapped pieces rigid until the solder cools and sets.

## Feeler Gauges

**Standard Feeler Gauge**        **Stepped Feeler Gauge**

JDPX3094

*Fig. 81 — Feeler Gauge Sets*

Feeler gauges (Fig. 81) are precision measuring tools for checking small clearances.

**Standard** feeler gauges have several blades arranged around a common pivot. Thickness of each blade is marked in thousandths of an inch or millimeters.

For example, a "0.006" indicates six-thousandths of an inch. A blade marked "6" indicates the same thing. On metric feeler gauges, a 0.15 indicates fifteen-hundredths of a millimeter.

**Stepped** feeler gauges have blades that have two thicknesses (Fig. 76). The tip of the blade is one thickness, while the rest of the blade is two-thousandths of an inch thicker. These feeler gauges are convenient for making quick, approximate measurements.

For thicknesses more than about 25 thousandths of an inch (1 mm), **wire** feeler gauges are often used. An example is a spark plug gap gauge.

### USE OF FEELER GAUGES

Never get the blades of the gauge wedged in the clearance space. If the blade being tried cannot enter the space without being forced, use a thinner blade, or adjust clearance to conform.

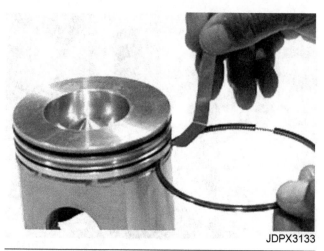

JDPX3133

*Fig. 82 — Use of Feeler Gauge*

Never bend or twist the blades. Always move the feeler gauge body in the same plane as the blade being used. Fig. 82 shows a feeler gauge being used correctly.

### CARE OF FEELER GAUGES

When in doubt about the thickness of a blade, measure it with a micrometer.

Occasionally wipe the blades clean with an oily cloth to remove dirt and prevent rusting.

## Micrometers

Micrometers or "mikes" are precision tools that measure in thousandths of an inch.

We will cover four types of micrometers:

- Outside Micrometers
- Inside Micrometers
- Telescope Gauges
- Depth Micrometers

Let's look at each one in detail.

## OUTSIDE MICROMETERS

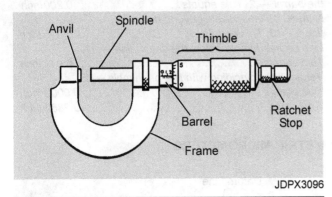

Fig. 83 — Outside Micrometer

An outside micrometer (Fig. 83) is used to measure the size of parts (diameter, thickness, etc.) accurately to within a very minute part of an inch.

**How to use:** Before measuring a part, determine the size of micrometer needed. Micrometer sizes are determined by the distance between faces of anvil and spindle when the thimble is screwed to both zero extremes of barrel. An accurate 1- to 2-inch (25 to 50 mm) micrometer will always have a minimum of one inch (25 mm) between faces and a maximum of two inches (50 mm). It cannot be used for measuring a part less than one inch (25 mm) thick.

After selecting the correct micrometer, open it up to a distance a little *greater* than the thickness of the part to be measured. With the micrometer held in one hand, bring it over the object to be measured.

*NOTE: One or both hands can be used to operate the micrometer.*

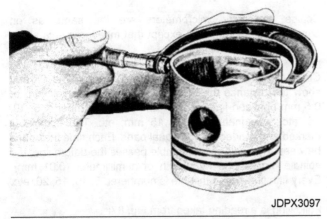

Fig. 84 — Correct Use of Outside Micrometer

Turn thimble lightly between the thumb and first finger until faces of anvil and spindle contact the work (Fig. 84). If the micrometer is equipped with a ratchet stop, turn it until at least two clicks can be heard.

Some micrometers do not have a ratchet stop; in this case a "feel" has to be developed to know when the correct contact pressure is being made by the spindle.

**IMPORTANT: Never tighten spindle so tight that work cannot be drawn from between anvil and spindle.**

Do not slide the micrometer back and forth excessively across the work, because this will wear away the face of both the anvil and spindle.

If possible, take the reading before removing the micrometer from the work, to obtain a more accurate reading. If the reading cannot be taken before removing the micrometer, remove it very carefully to prevent disturbing the position of the spindle.

In hard-to-reach places, use outside calipers to take a more accurate measure; then transfer to an inside micrometer for the reading.

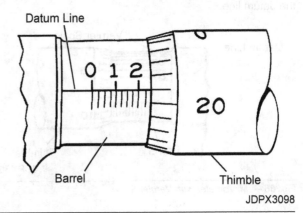

Fig. 85 — Micrometer Graduations

The graduations on a micrometer will be easier to understand when its construction is known. Micrometers use the principle of accurately cut screw-threads to determine measurement. Fig. 85 shows the barrel and thimble of a micrometer used to measure thousandths of an inch. This micrometer has 40 threads to an inch cut on the barrel and thimble. For construction and use of metric micrometers, see discussion beginning on next page.

Movement of the thimble on the barrel is limited to one inch. One complete revolution of the thimble is 1/40 part of an inch or 0.025 inch. The position of the thimble in relation to the barrel is used to read measurements.

The line marked lengthwise on the barrel is known as the revolution or datum line (Fig. 85).

Cross markings on this line show the distance the thimble travels in one revolution, or 0.025 inch between two lines. Every fourth line is numbered 1, 2, 3, etc., designating 0.100, 0.200, 0.300, etc. inch. The thimble is marked and divided into 25 equal parts. Each time the space between two lines on the thimble passes the datum line, the spindle moves one thousandth of an inch (0.001 inch). Every fifth line on the thimble is numbered 0, 5,10,15, and 20.

Following is an example of a reading taken from Fig. 85:

*Highest figure whose reference line is visible on barrel — 2. This equals* . . . . . . . . . . . . . . . . . . . *0.200 inch*
*Number of lines visible on barrel beyond highest figure — 1. This equals* . . . . . . . . . . . . . . . . . . . *0.025 inch*
*Line on thimble aligning with revolution of datum line — 21. This equals* . . . . . . . . . . . . . . . . . . . *0.021 inch*
*Total* . . . . . . . . . . . . . . . . . . . . . . . . . . . . . *0.246 inch*

If the line on the thimble does not align with the datum line, use the value that comes closest to it, or estimate the fraction of a thousandth over the line on the thimble below the datum line.

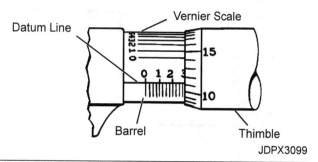

Fig. 86 — Micrometer with Vernier Scale

JDPX3099

If more accurate readings are desired, use a **vernier** micrometer (Fig. 86). This micrometer has a vernier scale on the barrel, which divides thousandths on the thimble into tenths making it possible to make a measurement to one ten-thousandth inch (0.0001 inch).

Take the value of the line on the thimble that falls below the datum line and add to this the value of the vernier scale reading. To determine the vernier scale reading, look along the edge of the thimble and find any vernier line and thimble line that coincide. For example, if the vernier line number 2 is found to coincide with a line on the thimble, then the vernier value is 0.0002 in.

Following is an example of a reading taken from Fig. 86:

*Highest figure whose reference line is visible in the barrel — 2. This equals* . . . . . . . . . . . . . . . . . *0.200 inch*
*Number of lines visible beyond highest figure — 3. This equals* . . . . . . . . . . . . . . . . . . . *0.075 inch*
*Line on the thimble below the datum line — 11. This equals* . . . . . . . . . . . . . . . . . . . . . . . . . . . *0.011 inch*
*Vernier line coinciding with line on thimble — 2. This equals* . . . . . . . . . . . . . . . . . . . . . . . . . *0.0002 inch*
*Total* . . . . . . . . . . . . . . . . . . . . . . . . . . . . . *0.2862 inch*

## METRIC MICROMETERS

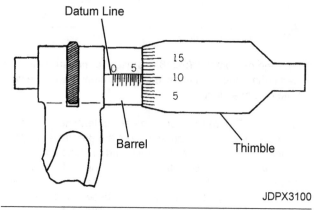

Fig. 87 — Barrel and Thimble of Metric Micrometer

JDPX3100

Fig. 87 shows the barrel and thimble of a metric micrometer used to measure hundredths of a millimeter. This micrometer contains threads every 0.5 mm.

Movement of the thimble on the barrel is limited to 25 mm. One complete revolution of the thimble is 0.5 mm. The position of the thimble in relation to the barrel is used to read measurements.

Scales on metric micrometers are the same as on conventional micrometers except that measurements are in millimeters instead of inches.

Cross markings appear below the datum line in Fig. 87 and show the distance the thimble travels in one revolution, or 0.5 mm between lines. Every tenth line is numbered 5, 10, 15, etc., designating 5, 10, 15 mm, etc. The thimble is marked and divided into 50 equal parts. Each time the space between two lines on the thimble passes the datum line, the spindle moves one hundredth of a millimeter (0.01 mm). Every fifth line on the thimble is numbered 5, 10, 15, 20, etc.

Following is a reading taken from Fig. 87:

*Highest figure whose reference line is visible on barrel — 5. This equals* . . . . . . . . . . . . . . . . . *5.00 mm*
*Number of lines visible on barrel beyond highest figure — 3. This equals* . . . . . . . . . . . . . . *1.50 mm*
*Line on thimble aligning with revolution of datum line — 11. This equals* . . . . . . . . . . . . . . . *0.11 mm*
*Total* . . . . . . . . . . . . . . . . . . . . . . . . . . . . . *6.61 mm*

If the line on the thimble does not align with the datum line, use the value that comes closest to it, or estimate the fraction of a hundredth over the line on the thimble below the datum line.

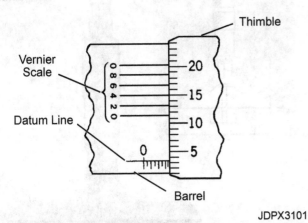

Fig. 88 — Vernier Micrometer

If more accurate readings are desired, use a **vernier micrometer** (Fig. 88). The vernier scale divides hundredths on the thimble into tenths, making it possible to measure to one thousandth millimeter.

Take the value of the line on the thimble that falls below the datum line and add to this the value of the vernier scale reading. To determine the vernier scale reading, look along the edge of the thimble and find any vernier line and thimble line that coincide. For example, if the vernier line number 2 is found to coincide with a line on the thimble, then the vernier value is 0.0002.

Following is an example of a reading taken from Fig. 88:

Highest figure whose reference line is visible
in the barrel — 0. This equals . . . . . . . . . . . . . . . . . . . .0mm
Number of lines visible beyond the highest
figure — 7. This equals . . . . . . . . . . . . . . . . . . . . . 3.5 mm
Line on thimble below the datum line — 3.
This equals . . . . . . . . . . . . . . . . . . . . . . . . . . . . 0.03 mm
Vernier line coinciding with line on thimble — 4.
This equals . . . . . . . . . . . . . . . . . . . . . . . . . . . 0.004 mm
Total . . . . . . . . . . . . . . . . . . . . . . . . . . . . . . . 3.534 mm

## DIGITAL CALIPERS AND MICROMETERS

Digital calipers and micrometers show the measured distance on a small display screen. They can show measurements in both inches and metric units.

## INSIDE MICROMETERS

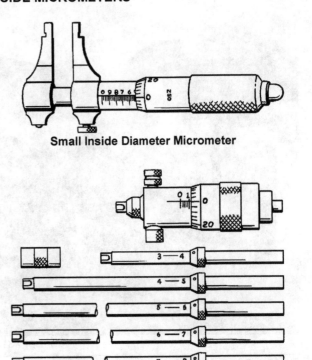

**Small Inside Diameter Micrometer**

**Large Inside Diameter Micrometer**

Fig. 89 — Inside Micrometers

There are two types of inside micrometers: one for measuring small diameters and one for large diameters (Fig. 89).

Each type is read exactly like the outside micrometer and must receive the same care.

IMPORTANT: **Never adjust an inside micrometer so tight that it cannot be withdrawn from the work.**

In hard-to-reach places, use an inside caliper to take the measurement; then transfer to an outside micrometer for the reading.

## TELESCOPE GAUGE

JDPX3103

*Fig. 90 — Telescope Gauge*

The telescope gauge (Fig. 90) is used to measure bores or openings. Place gauge in opening, expand to proper setting, lock by turning stem. This gauge has no scale markings. Measure the setting with an outside micrometer.

## DEPTH MICROMETER

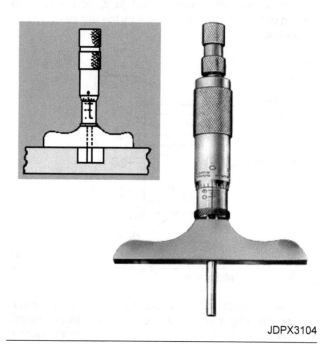

JDPX3104

*Fig. 91 — Using Depth Micrometer*

Depth micrometers (Fig. 91) are used to measure the depth of the openings.

Place the base of the micrometer firmly on the flat surface and turn down the thimble until the pin just touches the bottom of opening. Take the reading in the same way as with an outside micrometer.

When using micrometers, you must convert fractions to their decimal equivalents. (Refer to the decimal chart in weights and measures at the back of this book.)

## CARING FOR MICROMETERS

1. Avoid placing micrometers where they will become heated. This will affect their accuracy.

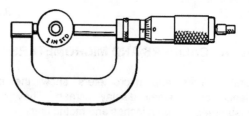

JDPX3105

*Fig. 92 — Checking Micrometer with Standard*

2. Check micrometers periodically with a master gauge or standard, to ensure accuracy (Fig. 92).

3. Keep micrometers in a case or box when not in use. This will protect them from grit and dirt.

4. Never allow a micrometer to become rusty or dirty. Wipe with a clean cloth oiled with a few drops of fine machine oil.

5. Always be sure micrometer faces that contact the work are clean before measuring. Never use anything abrasive for wiping faces clean.

**IMPORTANT:** **If a micrometer is accidentally dropped, never use it again until it has been checked on a master gauge or standard.**

## Dial Indicators

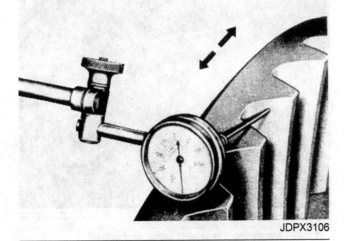

JDPX3106

*Fig. 93 — Dial Indicator Measuring Backlash on a Gear*

Dial indicators measure the movement in shafts or gears that have adjustable endplay or backlash (Fig. 93).

Some indicators have C-clamps for mounting them, while others have a magnetic mount.

Be sure to mount the indicator securely and at right angles to the moving part. This will ensure that the full movement is registered on the dial.

To record the full movement, also be sure to pry the parts in both directions, noting the full range of movement on the indicator dial.

## Spring Testers

Spring testers check springs for resiliency to see if they match the specifications. Engine valve springs, for example, should all be of uniform strength to allow the valves to work smoothly.

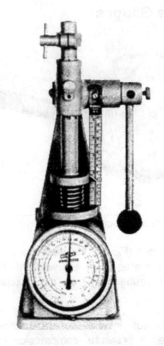

JDPX3107

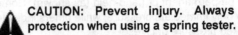

*Fig. 94 — Using a Spring Tester*

⚠ **CAUTION: Prevent injury. Always wear eye protection when using a spring tester.**

To use the tester (Fig. 94), insert the spring, pull on the lever to compress the spring to the specified compressed length, and read on the dial the pounds of pressure exerted.

Never use the stop on the tester to fix the length to which the spring is to be compressed. The stop should only be used when comparing one spring with another.

### CARING FOR SPRING TESTERS

Zero is adjustable on most spring testers by moving a small lever or other device on the dial.

Normally, the pointer can also be tapped into position if it does not match the zero mark after the adjustment above.

Check the scale pointer occasionally to make sure it is correct.

## Pressure Gauges

JDPX3108

*Fig. 95 — Pressure Gauge (Oil Pressure Type Shown)*

Pressure gauges (Fig. 95) measure the force exerted on an enclosure by the liquid or gas within it. This is usually in "pounds per square inch" or "psi" (kilopascal or kPa in metric).

Pressure gauges include those to check oil pressure (shown), tire air pressure, compression pressure, cooling system pressure, and fuel pressure.

Gauges may be permanent or hand-held (as shown). Some gauges show only immediate pressure, while others indicate the last-checked pressure until reset.

Pressure gauges should never be oiled. However, keep out all dirt and corrosion to ensure an accurate reading.

## Compression Tester

Compression testers measure an engine's compression in a given cylinder. They are used to diagnose a poorly sealed cylinder, which can result in a loss of power and mean that an engine requires a rebuild.

There are two types of compression testers. One is threaded and screws into the spark plug hole. The other is a hand-held tester with a rubber tip to form a seal over the spark plug opening.

## Speed-Measuring Tools

Shop tools used for measuring speed are available in many shapes and forms. The following are discussed here:

- Tachometers
- Mechanical Hand-Held Digital Tachometers
- Photo Tachometers
- Vibration Tachometers
- Stroboscopes (Timing Lights)

- Oscilloscopes
- Electronic Tachometers

**Tachometers** show the revolutions compared to a time increment (as rpm). Another example of this is the common speedometer, which indicates wheel revolutions per hour, computed in miles per hour (mph). Tachometers on most machines, however, give engine speed in revolutions per minute (rpm).

JDPX3109

*Fig. 96 — Mechanical Hand-Held Digital Tachometer*

The simplest tool for measuring speeds is the **mechanical hand-held digital tachometer** (Fig. 96). When taking a reading, the rubber-tipped shaft is pressed against the end of the revolving shaft. The number of revolutions is noted on the digital display as revolutions per minute (rpm).

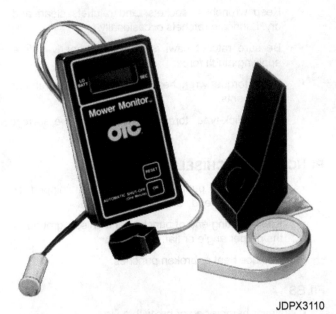

JDPX3110

*Fig. 97 — Electronic Photo Tachometer*

A **photo tachometer** (Fig. 97) is a highly accurate instrument used to check rpm and stopping time. The equipment uses a photo (light) probe and reflective tape. The meter measures the time between each pass of the tape.

JDPX3111

*Fig. 98 — Vibration Tachometer*

The **vibration tachometer** (Fig. 98) (sirometer) will indicate the revolutions per minute (rpm) of revolving equipment by matching rpm to vibration frequency. Place the vibration tachometer on a level surface of the operating equipment. When the adjustable length of wire resonates consistently with the equipment, the rpm is read on the tachometer scale.

The **stroboscope** gives speed of rotation or vibration. It does not touch the device it is checking, but uses a rapidly flashing light. To determine the rotating speed of a shaft, for example, the speed of the flashing light is adjusted until the shaft appears to stand still. In other words, the speed of the shaft is synchronized to the flashing light. The speed of the shaft can then be read on the dial of the stroboscope.

A **timing light** operates the same as a stroboscope except that it receives its power and timing impulses from the machine being tested. Timing lights are commonly used to test and adjust the ignition timing of engines.

An **oscilloscope** measures speeds from slow heartbeats to high ratio frequencies. It is widely used in testing the vibrations in various parts of a test engine or other components. A common time signal (such as a 60-cycle current) is used for comparison against the unknown time cycle. This comparison is displayed on a cathode ray tube.

**Electronic tachometers** measure speed in a variety of ways. One type has an inductive pick-up sensor clamped to the fuel injection pump line. The sensor "reads" the fuel pulsation in the line and sends a signal to the digital meter. Another type requires no hook-up. A sensor is located in the meter. When the meter is held near the spark plug wire, the sensor picks up the electrical pulses in the wire. The meter times the pulses and then displays the rpm.

## SPECIAL TOOLS

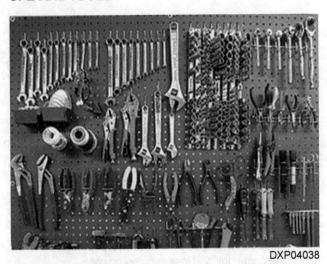

DXP04038

*Fig. 99 — Special Tools Are Also Needed to Completely Equip the Shop*

There is one category of shop tools that we have not covered — the **special tools** (Fig. 99) recommended for specific jobs in the shop. This includes both test equipment and specialized repair tools.

In this chapter we have covered only the basic shop tools that are widely used in the shop. For more complex tools, refer to the EQS manuals on such subjects as "Electrical Systems" and "Engines." And for special repair tools, refer to the machine technical manual to perform the job properly.

# Tool Care

As stated in the beginning of this book, tools don't make the service technician, but they help. Worn or damaged tools are of no help. In many cases they are a hindrance. Did you ever try to remove a nut with a cracked or rounded socket? The nut usually remains tight but the corners get rounded off.

Proper care is an important part of every technician's career. Keep tools in usable, safe condition. In a shop environment, tools can be used by many other people. Keep the respect of fellow service people by using tools properly and return them in good condition to their respective shelf or area.

Let's quickly review proper use and care of shop tools:

## SCREWDRIVERS

- Don't use screwdrivers for prying, punching, chiseling, scoring, or scraping.
- Use the correct tipped screwdriver for the fastener to be turned.
- Keep handles clean.
- Keep screwdrivers organized to find the proper screwdriver quickly.

## HAMMERS

- Never strike a hammer on a hardened part or another hammer.
- Grasp handle near the end and strike object with full face of hammer.
- Discard hammer when face is chipped or mushroomed.

## PLIERS

- Avoid using pliers on hardened surfaces; teeth become dull and lose gripping power.
- Keep clean and oil pivot pin occasionally.

## WRENCHES

- Never use a "cheater bar" on a wrench handle.
- Never cock a wrench; be sure it is positioned squarely on fastener.
- Never hammer on a wrench; use a striking wrench.
- Orient an adjustable wrench so greater force is on the fixed jaw.
- Replace any spread, worn, or damaged sockets and wrenches.
- Do not use hand (chrome) sockets on power or impact tools.
- Select proper wrench or socket for the fastener to be turned, especially for metric hardware.
- Keep wrenches, sockets, and ratchets clean and dry. Lubricate ratchets occasionally.
- Be sure ratchet pawl is engaged properly before applying much force.
- Treat torque wrenches as delicate measurement instruments.
- Store click-type torque wrenches at the lowest setting.

## PUNCHES AND CHISELS

- Never use a punch or chisel with a chipped or mushroomed end. Grind tool end down.
- Keep working end of punches and chisels ground to the proper angle or flat.
- Replace bent or broken punches.

## FILES

- Never hammer on or pry with a file.
- Keep file teeth clean and handle tight.
- Keep files neatly stored, away from moisture and oil.

## HACKSAWS

- Keep blade tightly stretched.
- Wipe blade with oily cloth to prevent rust.
- Store hacksaw carefully to prevent injury or damaged teeth.

## VISES AND CLAMPS

- Do not hammer on handle to tighten or loosen.
- Use large enough vise or clamp for the particular job.
- Use wood or soft jaws if object to be held may be marred.

## TWIST DRILLS

- Use proper feeding speed for the type of drill used.
- Use lubricant to cool drill when possible.
- Replace or sharpen damaged or dull drill bits.

## TAPS AND DIES

- Use proper size tap drill.
- Lubricate tap and die during use.
- Use proper style tap for the job to be done.

## SCREW EXTRACTORS

- Drill an exactly centered, properly sized hole.
- Do not heat extractor.

## PULLERS

- Choose right type and size of puller.
- Be sure puller is secure before applying force.
- Don't overload puller.

## PICK-UP TOOLS

- Keep stored in an accessible area and in clean condition.

## MIRRORS

- Protect mirror from damage.

## TUBING CUTTERS

- Use slow, even pressure to cut tubing.
- Replace cutter wheel when dull or damaged.

## FEELER GAUGES

- Never bend or twist blades. Do not force a blade into an opening.
- Wipe blades occasionally to remove dirt and prevent rusting.

## MICROMETERS AND DIAL INDICATORS

- Do not put micrometers and dial indicators where they will become heated.
- Never drop a micrometer. Check a dropped micrometer before using it again.
- Wipe micrometer with clean cloth and light machine oil.
- Store precision measuring instruments in a case.

## SPRING TESTER

- Treat as any other precision measurement instrument.
- Use stop only when making spring comparisons.

## PRESSURE GAUGES

- Store in protected case to prevent damage to gauge case and glass.
- Keep parts plugged to prevent contamination or damage.

## SPEED MEASURING TOOLS

- Store tools safely in cases.
- Protect from dirt, oil, or moisture.
- Turn electronic devices off to preserve battery life.

## TOOL CABINETS AND STORAGE AREAS

- Keep tools in proper areas and in an organized manner.
- Keep floor clean and oil-free.
- Advise supervisor of any damaged or missing tools immediately.
- Request any additional tools necessary to complete a job as soon as possible.

## Safety

Safety in the shop is a must! Safe practices and common sense must be exercised at all times.

JDPX3113

*Fig. 100 — Use Safety Glasses with Side Shields When Grinding*

## SHOP SAFETY

First we will discuss general shop safety.

## Be Prepared for Emergencies

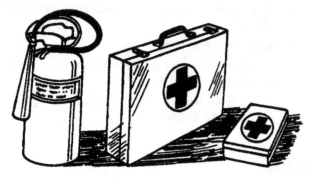

JDPX3114

*Fig. 101 — Be Prepared*

Be prepared if a fire starts.

Keep a first aid kit and fire extinguisher handy. Keep emergency numbers for doctors, ambulance service, hospital, and fire department near your telephone.

## Wear Protective Clothing

JDPX3115

*Fig. 102 — Wear Protective Clothing*

Wear close-fitting clothing and safety equipment appropriate to the job.

Prolonged exposure to loud noise can cause impairment or loss of hearing.

Wear a suitable hearing protective device such as earmuffs or earplugs to protect against objectionable or uncomfortable loud noises.

## Use Equipment Safely

JDPX3116

*Fig. 103 — Use Equipment Safely*

Tie long hair behind your head. Do not wear a necktie, scarf, loose clothing, or necklace when you work near machine tools or moving parts. If these items were to get caught, severe injury could result.

Remove rings and other jewelry to prevent electrical shorts and entanglement in moving parts.

## Work in Clean, Ventilated Area

JDPX3117

*Fig. 104 — Work in Clean, Ventilated Area*

Before starting a job:

- Clean work area and machine.

- Make sure you have all necessary tools to do your job.

- Have the right parts on hand.

- Read all instructions thoroughly; do not attempt shortcuts.

Engine exhaust fumes can cause sickness or death. If it is necessary to run an engine in an enclosed area, remove the exhaust fumes from the area with an exhaust pipe extension.

If you do not have an exhaust pipe extension, open the doors and get outside air into the area.

## Illuminate Work Area Safely

JDPX3118

*Fig. 105 — Illuminate Work Area Safely*

Illuminate your work area adequately but safely. Use a portable safety light for working inside or under a machine. Make sure the bulb is enclosed by a wire cage. The hot filament of an accidentally broken bulb can ignite spilled fuel or oil.

## Practice Safe Maintenance

Understand service procedure before doing work. Keep area clean and dry.

Keep hands, feet, and clothing away from power-driven parts. Disconnect all power and operate controls to relieve any pressure. Lower equipment to the ground. Stop the engine. Remove the key. Allow machine to cool.

Securely support any machine elements that must be raised for service work.

Keep all parts in good condition and properly installed. Fix damage immediately. Replace worn or broken parts. Remove any buildup of grease, oil, or debris.

Disconnect battery ground cable (–) or power supply before making adjustments on electrical systems or welding on machine.

## Use Proper Tools

Use tools appropriate to the work. Makeshift tools and procedures can create safety hazards.

Use power tools only to loosen threaded parts and fasteners.

For loosening and tightening hardware, use the correct size tools. DO NOT use U.S. measurement tools on metric fasteners. Avoid bodily injury caused by slipping wrenches.

## Use Only Recommended Service Replacement Parts

JDPX3119

*Fig. 106 — Use Proper Tools*

## Support Equipment Properly

JDPX3120

*Fig. 107 — Support Equipment Properly*

Before working on the machine:

- Lower all equipment to the ground.

- Stop the engine and remove the key if equipped.

- Disconnect the battery ground strap or power supply.

- Hang a "DO NOT OPERATE" tag at operator station.

Always lower the machine or attachment to the ground before you work on the machine. If you must work on a lifted machine or attachment, securely support the machine or attachment with properly rated floor stands.

Do not support the machine on cinder blocks, hollow tiles, or props that may crumble under continuous load. Do not work under a machine that is supported solely by a jack. Follow recommended procedures in technical manual.

Lifting heavy components incorrectly can cause severe injury or machine damage.

Follow recommended procedure for removal and installation of components in the manual.

## Handle Fluids Safely—Avoid Fires

JDPX3121

*Fig. 108 — Handle Fluids Safely*

When you work around fuel, do not smoke or work near heaters or other fire hazards.

Store flammable fluids away from fire hazards. Do not incinerate or puncture pressurized containers.

Make sure machine is clean of trash, grease, and debris.

Do not store oily rags; they can ignite and burn spontaneously.

## Avoid High-Pressure Fluids

JDPX3122

*Fig. 109 — Avoid High-Pressure Fluids*

Escaping fluid under pressure can penetrate the skin causing serious injury.

Avoid the hazard by relieving pressure before disconnecting hydraulic or other lines. Tighten all connections before applying pressure.

Search for leaks with a piece of cardboard. Protect hands and body from high-pressure fluids.

If an accident occurs, see a doctor immediately. Any fluid injected into the skin must be surgically removed within a few hours or gangrene may result. Doctors unfamiliar with this type of injury should reference a knowledgeable medical source.

## Remove Paint Before Welding or Heating

JDPX3123

*Fig. 110 — Remove Paint Before Welding or Heating*

Avoid potentially toxic fumes and dust.

Hazardous fumes can be generated when paint is heated by welding, soldering, or using a torch.

Do all work outside or in a well-ventilated area. Dispose of paint and solvent properly.

Remove paint before welding or heating:

- If you sand or grind paint, avoid breathing the dust. Wear an approved respirator.

- If you use solvent or paint stripper, remove stripper with soap and water before welding. Remove solvent or paint stripper containers and other flammable material from area. Allow fumes to disperse at least 15 minutes before welding or heating.

## Avoid Heating Near Pressurized Fluid Lines

JDPX3124

Fig. 111 — Avoid Heating Near Pressurized Fluid Lines

Flammable spray can be generated by heating near pressurized fluid lines, resulting in severe burns to you and bystanders. Do not heat by welding, soldering, or using a torch near pressurized fluid lines or other flammable materials.

Pressurized lines can be accidentally cut when heat goes beyond the immediate flame area. Install fire resisting guards to protect hoses or other materials.

## Service Air Pressurized Equipment Safely

JDPX3125

Fig. 112 — Service Air-Pressurized Equipment Safely

Explosive separation of a tire and rim parts can cause serious injury or death.

Do not attempt to mount a tire unless you have the proper equipment and experience to perform the job.

Always maintain the correct tire pressure. Do not inflate the tires above the recommended pressure. Never weld or heat a wheel and tire assembly. The heat can cause an increase in air pressure resulting in a tire explosion. Welding can structurally weaken or deform the wheel.

When inflating tires, use a clip-on chuck and extension hose long enough to allow you to stand to one side and NOT in front of or over the tire assembly. Use a safety cage if available.

Check wheels for low pressure, cuts, bubbles, damaged rims, or missing lug bolts and nuts.

## Prevent Battery Explosions

JDPX3126

Fig. 113 — Prevent Battery Explosions

Keep sparks, lighted matches, and open flame away from the top of battery. Battery gas can explode.

Never check battery charge by placing a metal object across the posts. Use a voltmeter or hydrometer.

Do not charge a frozen battery; it may explode. Warm battery to 16°C (60°F) first.

## Prevent Acid Burns

Sulfuric acid in battery electrolyte is poisonous. It is strong enough to burn skin, eat holes in clothing, and cause blindness if splashed into eyes.

Avoid the hazard by:

1. Filling batteries in a well-ventilated area.

2. Wearing eye protection and rubber gloves.

3. Avoiding breathing fumes when electrolyte is added.

4. Avoiding spilling or dripping electrolyte.

5. Use proper jump-start procedure.

If you spill acid on yourself:

1. Flush your skin with water.

2. Apply baking soda or lime to help neutralize the acid.

3. Flush your eyes with water for 10-15 minutes. Get medical attention immediately.

If acid is swallowed:

1. Drink large amounts of water or milk.

2. Then drink milk of magnesia, beaten eggs, or vegetable oil.

3. Get medical attention immediately.

## Avoid Harmful Asbestos Dust

JDPX3127

*Fig. 114 — Avoid Harmful Asbestos Dust*

Avoid breathing dust that may be generated when handling components containing asbestos fibers. Inhaled asbestos fibers may cause lung cancer.

Components in products that may contain asbestos fibers are brake pads, brake band and lining assemblies, clutch plates, and some gaskets. The asbestos used in these components is usually found in a resin or sealed in some way. Normal handling is not hazardous as long as airborne dust containing asbestos is not generated.

Avoid creating dust. Never use compressed air for cleaning. Avoid brushing or grinding of asbestos-containing materials. When servicing, wear an approved respirator. A special vacuum cleaner is recommended to clean asbestos. If not available, wet the asbestos-containing materials with a mist of oil or water.

Keep bystanders away from the area.

## Dispose of Fluids Properly

JDPX3128

*Fig. 115 — Dispose of Fluids Properly*

Improperly disposing of fluids can harm the environment and ecology. Before draining any fluids, find out the proper way to dispose of waste from your local environmental agency.

Use proper containers when draining fluids. Do not use food or beverage containers that may mislead someone into drinking from them.

DO NOT pour oil into the ground, down a drain, or into a stream, pond, or lake. Observe relevant environmental protection regulations when disposing of oil, fuel, coolant, brake fluid, filters, batteries, and other harmful waste.

## Live with Safety

JDPX3129

*Fig. 116 — Live with Safety*

Before returning machine to service or customer, make sure machine is functioning properly, especially the safety systems. Install all guards and shields.

## TOOL SAFETY

Strict adherence to tool safety makes the difference between a job well done or a serious injury. Not only using the right tool for the job, but using it correctly with the proper safety apparel is very important.

The following is a list of safety guidelines:

- Always wear safety goggles or glasses equipped with side shields when using punches, chisels, hammers, power tools, cutting tools, or grinders.

- Wear ear protection whenever noise levels are excessive; usually caused by power tool operation, machine noise or hammer blows.

- Wear a dust and/or vapor mask when appropriate; such as when grinding, welding, or when working around harmful vapors like cleaning solvents and spray paints.

- Wear appropriate apparel; loose clothing can get caught in moving parts.

- Use the right tool for the job.

- Keep tools sharp and in good shape. Keep them clean and well-adjusted. Make sure handles are securely fastened. Replace any cracked or broken tools.

- Screwdriver handles and ordinary plastic-dipped handles are not designed to act as insulation; don't use on live electrical circuits.

- Never use any tool as a hammer unless manufactured for that purpose.

- Never use a pipe extension or other form of "cheater" bar to increase the leverage of any wrench.

- Never use a hammer on any wrench, except one that's designed to be struck.

- Hold a chisel or punch with a tool holder if possible.

- Keep all guards in place and in good working order when operating power equipment.

- Don't pull on a tool cabinet to move it; push it in front of you.

- Before moving tool cabinet, close the lids, lock drawers and doors.

- Do not open more than one loaded drawer of a tool cabinet at a time. Close each drawer before opening another. Too many drawers opened at one time could cause the tool cabinet to tip over.

- Set the brakes on the locking casters after cabinet is positioned at your work place.

- Keep work area clean. Store tools not in use. Disconnect all power tools when not in use.

- Keep children or spectators a safe distance from the work area.

- Remember, horseplay in the shop can cause accidents.

## Test Yourself

### QUESTIONS

1. True or false? "If a screwdriver bit becomes rounded or broken, it can be reground."

2. What type of hammer should be used on machined surfaces?

3. True or false? "Pliers are used for tightening and loosening small nuts."

4. Should you normally pull or push on a wrench?

5. Why are the heads of open-end wrenches made with an offset?

6. True or false? "Adjustable wrenches can be used exactly like open-end wrenches by flopping them over for a new swing."

7. Match the two items that coincide with a. Torque and b. Tension below:

a. Torque    1. Straight pull    3. Foot-pounds (N•m)

b. Tension    2. Turning force    4. Pounds (N)

8. If a torque reading calls for 5 foot-pounds, how much is that in inch-pounds?

9. Which is the higher strength bolt – one with three dash marks on its head or one with six dashes?

10. When grinding a chisel (or a screwdriver bit), why should you not hold it against the grinding wheel for any great length of time?

11. When filing, should you do the cutting on the pushing or the pulling stroke?

12. When placing a hacksaw blade in its frame, should the saw teeth point toward the handle or away from it?

13. At least how many teeth should always contact the material when using a hacksaw?

14. What are the three types of pullers?

15. When pulling a bearing that is mounted against a flat housing, what attachment should be used with the puller?

16. Explain how two metals are joined when soldering.

17. What does a "6" indicate on the blade of a feeler gauge?

18. True or false? "When taking a reading with an outside micrometer, clamp it tightly over the work to be sure of an accurate reading."

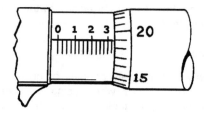

JDPX3130

*Fig. 117 — Micrometer Reading*

19. What is the measurement shown on the micrometer in Fig. 117?

20. What do "psi" and "kPa" mean?

**(Answers in Appendix B, "Answers to Test Yourself Questions.")**

# APPENDIX

## Weights and Measures

Here are most of the equivalent and conversion charts you will need in everyday shop work.

### FRACTIONS, DECIMALS, AND MILLIMETERS CHART

| Inches | | mm | Inches | | mm |
|--------|-------|-------|--------|-------|-------|
| 1/64 | 0.016 | 0.40 | 33/64 | 0.516 | 13.10 |
| 1/32 | 0.031 | 0.79 | 17/32 | 0.531 | 13.49 |
| 3/64 | 0.047 | 1.19 | 35/64 | 0.547 | 13.89 |
| 1/16 | 0.062 | 1.59 | 9/16 | 0.562 | 14.29 |
| 5/64 | 0.078 | 1.98 | 37/64 | 0.578 | 14.68 |
| 3/32 | 0.094 | 2.38 | 19/32 | 0.594 | 15.08 |
| | 0.100 | 2.54 | | 0.600 | 15.24 |
| 7/64 | 0.109 | 2.78 | 39/64 | 0.609 | 15.48 |
| 1/8 | 0.125 | 3.18 | 5/8 | 0.625 | 15.88 |
| 9/64 | 0.141 | 3.57 | 41/64 | 0.641 | 16.27 |
| 5/32 | 0.156 | 3.97 | 21/32 | 0.656 | 16.67 |
| 11/64 | 0.172 | 4.37 | 43/64 | 0.672 | 17.07 |
| 3/16 | 0.188 | 4.76 | 11/16 | 0.688 | 17.46 |
| 13/64 | 0.203 | 5.16 | 45/64 | 0.703 | 17.86 |
| 7/32 | 0.219 | 5.56 | 23/32 | 0.719 | 18.26 |
| 15/64 | 0.234 | 5.95 | 47/64 | 0.734 | 18.65 |
| 1/4 | 0.250 | 6.35 | 3/4 | 0.750 | 19.05 |
| 17/64 | 0.266 | 6.75 | 49/64 | 0.766 | 19.45 |
| 9/32 | 0.281 | 7.14 | 25/32 | 0.781 | 19.84 |
| 19/64 | 0.297 | 7.54 | 51/64 | 0.797 | 20.24 |
| 5/16 | 0.312 | 7.94 | 13/16 | 0.812 | 20.64 |
| 21/64 | 0.328 | 8.33 | 53/64 | 0.828 | 21.03 |
| 11/32 | 0.344 | 8.73 | 27/32 | 0.844 | 21.43 |
| 23/64 | 0.359 | 9.13 | 55/64 | 0.859 | 21.83 |
| 3/8 | 0.375 | 9.53 | 7/8 | 0.875 | 22.23 |
| 25/64 | 0.391 | 9.92 | 57/64 | 0.891 | 22.62 |
| | 0.400 | 10.16 | | 0.900 | 22.86 |
| 13/32 | 0.406 | 10.32 | 29/32 | 0.906 | 23.02 |
| 27/64 | 0.422 | 10.72 | 59/64 | 0.922 | 23.42 |
| 7/16 | 0.438 | 11.11 | 15/16 | 0.938 | 23.81 |
| 29/64 | 0.453 | 11.51 | 61/64 | 0.953 | 24.21 |
| 15/32 | 0.469 | 11.91 | 31/32 | 0.969 | 24.61 |
| 31/64 | 0.484 | 12.30 | 63/64 | 0.984 | 25.00 |
| 1/2 | 0.500 | 12.70 | 1 | 1.000 | 25.40 |

### WEIGHT MEASURE

1 Gross or Long Ton = 2240 Lb.

1 Net or Short Ton = 2000 Lb.

1 Cubic Foot of Water = 62.5 Lb.

1 Gallon of Water = 8.33 Lb.

### SQUARE MEASURE

1 Township = 36 Square Miles

1 Square Mile = 640 Acres

1 Acre = 4,840 Square Yards

1 Acre = 43,560 Square Feet

1 Square Yard = 9 Square Feet

1 Square Foot = 144 Square Inches

1 Hectare = 2.471 Acres

### SURVEYOR'S MEASURE

1 Link = 7.92 Inches

1 Rod = 25 Links 1

1 Chain = 4 Rods

1 Acre = 10 Square Chains

1 Acre = 160 Square Rods

1 Township = 36 Square Miles (6 Miles Square)

### LENGTH MEASURE

| | |
|---|---|
| 1 Mile = 8 Furlongs | 1 Chain = 4 Rods |
| 1 Mile = 80 Chains | 1 Chain = 22 Yards |
| 1 Mile = 320 Rods | 1 Chain = 66 Feet |
| 1 Mile = 1760 Yards | 1 Chain = 100 Links |
| 1 Furlong = 10 Chains | 1 Rod = 5.5 Yards |
| 1 Furlong = 220 Yards | 1 Rod = 16.5 Feet |
| 1 Station = 6.06 Rods | 1 Yard = 3 Feet |
| 1 Station = 33.3 Yards | 1 Yard = 36 Inches |
| 1 Station = 100 Feet | 1 Foot = 12 Inches |

## CUBIC MEASURE

1 Cubic Foot = 1728 Cubic Inches

1 Cubic Yard = 27 Cubic Feet

## DRY MEASURE

2 Pints = 1 Quart

8 Quarts = 1 Peck

4 Pecks = 1 Bushel

1 Bushel = 2150.42 Cubic Inches

## FLUID MEASURE

1 Teaspoon = 1/3 Tablespoon

1 Tablespoon = 1/2 Ounce

2 Cups = 1 Pint

16 Ounces = 1 Pint

2 Pints = 1 Quart

4 Quarts = 1 Gallon

1 Gallon = 231 Cubic Inches

1 Gallon = 0.1337 Cubic Foot

1 Cubic Foot = 7.5 Gallons

## METRIC WEIGHTS AND MEASURES

### Weight Measure

10 milligrams . . . . . . . . . . . . . . . . . . . . . . 1 centigram (cg)

10 centigrams. . . . . . . . 1 decigram (dg) — 100 milligrams

10 decigrams . . . . . . . . . . .1 gram (g) — 1000 milligrams

10 grams . . . . . . . . . . . . . . . . . . . . 1 dekagram (dkg)

10 dekagrams. . . . . . . . . 1 hectogram (hg) — 100 grams

10 hectograms . . . . . . . . . . 1 kilogram (kg) — 1000 grams

1000 kilograms. . . . . . . . . . . . . . . . . . . . .1 metric ton (t)

### Area Measure

100 square millimeters (mm$^2$) . . . . . . . . . . . . . . . .1 square centimeter (cm$^2$)

10 000 square centimeters . . . . . . . . . .1 square meter (m$^2$) — 1,000,000 square millimeters

100 square meters . . . . . . . . . . . . . . . . . . . . . 1 are (a)

100 ares . . . . . . . . 1 hectare (ha) — 10,000 square meters

100 hectares . . . . . . . . . . . . . . . . 1 square kilometer (km$^2$) — 1,000,000 square meters

### Linear Measure

10 millimeters (mm). . . . . . . . . . . . . . . . . .1 centimeter (cm)

10 centimeters. . . . . . . 1 decimeter (dm) — 100 millimeters

10 decimeters . . . . . . . . . . .1 meter (m) — 1000 millimeters

10 meters . . . . . . . . . . . . . . . . . . . . .1 dekameter (dkm)

10 hectometers . . . . . . . . 1 kilometer (km) — 1000 meters

### Cubic Measure

1000 cubic millimeters (mm$^3$) . . . . . . cubic centimeter (cm$^3$)

1000 cubic centimeters . . . . . . . . . .1 cubic decimeter (dm$^3$) — 1,000,000 cubic millimeters

1000 cubic decimeters . . . . . . . . . . . . . . 1 cubic meter (m$^3$) 1 stere — 1,000,000 cubic centimeters — 1,000,000,000 cubic millimeters

### Volume Measure

10 milliliters (mL) . . . . . . . . . . . . . . . . . . . . .1 centiliter (cL)

10 centiliters . . . . . . . . . . . . . . . . . . . . . . . . . .1 deciliter (dL) — 100 milliliters

10 deciliters . . . . . . . . . . . . . . .1 liter (L) — 1000 milliliters

10 dekaliters . . . . . . . . . . . . . 1 hectoliter (hL) — 100 liters

10 hectoliters. . . . . . . . . . . . . . 1 kiloliter (kL) — 1000 liters

# Measurement Conversion Chart

## Metric to English

### Length
1 millimeter = 0.03937 inches. . . . . . . . . . . . . . . . . . . . . . in
1 meter = 3.281 feet . . . . . . . . . . . . . . . . . . . . . . . . . . . ft
1 kilometer = 0.621 miles . . . . . . . . . . . . . . . . . . . . . . .mi

### Area
1 meter$^2$ = 10.76 feet$^2$ . . . . . . . . . . . . . . . . . . . . . . .ft$^2$
1 hectare = 2.471 acres . . . . . . . . . . . . . . . . . . . . . . acre
    (hectare = 10,000 m$^2$)

### Mass (Weight)
1 kilogram = 2.205 pounds. . . . . . . . . . . . . . . . . . . . . . lb
1 tonne (1000 kg) = 1.102 short ton . . . . . . . . . . . . . .sh tn

### Volume
1 meter$^3$ = 35.31 foot$^3$ . . . . . . . . . . . . . . . . . . . . . . . .ft$^3$
1 meter$^3$ = 1.308 yard$^3$. . . . . . . . . . . . . . . . . . . . . . .yd$^3$
1 meter$^3$ = 28.38 bushel. . . . . . . . . . . . . . . . . . . . . . . bu
1 liter = 0.02838 bushel . . . . . . . . . . . . . . . . . . . . . . . bu
1 liter = 1.057 quart . . . . . . . . . . . . . . . . . . . . . . . . . . qt

### Pressure
1 kilopascal = 0.145 pound/in$^2$ . . . . . . . . . . . . . . . . . . psi

### Stress
1 megapascal or
1 newton/millimeter$^2$ = 145 pound/in$^2$ . . . . . . . . . . . . . psi
    (1N/mm$^2$ = 1MPa)

### Power
1 kilowatt = 1.341 horsepower (550 lb-ft/s) . . . . . . . . . . hp
    (1 watt = 1 N•m/sec)

### Energy (Work)
1 joule = 0.0009478 British Thermal Unit . . . . . . . . . . . .Btu
    (1 J = 1 W s)

### Force
1 newton = 0.2248 pounds force . . . . . . . . . . . . . . . .lb force

### Torque or Bending Moment
1 newton meter = 0.7376 foot-pound . . . . . . . . . . . . . . lb-ft

### Temperature
$t_C = (t_F - 32)/1.8$

## English To Metric

### Length
1 inch = 25.4 millimeters . . . . . . . . . . . . . . . . . . . . . . .mm
1 foot = 0.3048 meters . . . . . . . . . . . . . . . . . . . . . . . . . m
1 yard = 0.9144 meters . . . . . . . . . . . . . . . . . . . . . . . . . m
1 mile = 1.608 kilometers . . . . . . . . . . . . . . . . . . . . . . .km

### Area
1 foot$^2$ = 0.0929 meter$^2$ . . . . . . . . . . . . . . . . . . . . . . .m$^2$
1 acre = 0.4047 hectare . . . . . . . . . . . . . . . . . . . . . . . ha
    (hectare = 10,000 m$^2$)

### Mass (Weight)
1 pound = 0.4535 kilograms . . . . . . . . . . . . . . . . . . . . . kg
1 ton (2000 lb) = 0.9071 tonnes . . . . . . . . . . . . . . . . . . t

### Volume
1 foot$^3$ = 0.02832 meter$^3$ . . . . . . . . . . . . . . . . . . . . . .m$^3$
1 yard$^3$ = 0.7646 meter$^3$ . . . . . . . . . . . . . . . . . . . . . .m$^3$
1 bushel = 0.03524 meter$^3$ . . . . . . . . . . . . . . . . . . . . .m$^3$
1 bushel = 35.24 liter. . . . . . . . . . . . . . . . . . . . . . . . . .L
1 quart = 0.9464 liter. . . . . . . . . . . . . . . . . . . . . . . . . .L
1 gallon = 3.785 liter . . . . . . . . . . . . . . . . . . . . . . . . . .L

### Pressure
1 pound/inch$^2$ = 6.895 kilopascals. . . . . . . . . . . . . . . .kPa
1 pound/inch$^2$ = 0.06895 bars. . . . . . . . . . . . . . . . . . . bar

### Stress
1 pound/in$^2$ (psi) = 0.006895 megapascal . . . . . . . . . . MPa
             or newton/mm$^2$ . . . . . . . . . . . . . N/mm$^2$
    (1 N/mm$^2$ = 1 MPa)

### Power
1 horsepower (550 lb-ft/s) = 0.7457 kilowatt . . . . . . . . . . kW
    (1 watt = 1 N•m/s)

### Energy (Work)
1 British Thermal Unit = 1055 joules . . . . . . . . . . . . . . . . . J
    (1 J = 1 W s)

### Force
1 pound = 4.448 newtons . . . . . . . . . . . . . . . . . . . . . . . .N

### Torque or Bending Moment
1 pound-foot = 1.356 newton-meters . . . . . . . . . . . . . . .N•m

### Temperature
$t_F = 1.8 \times t_C + 32$

## Miscellaneous Fastener Torque Values

| Fastener | Type | Minimum Tensile Strength | Material | Body Size or Outside Diameter | | | | | | | | | |
|---|---|---|---|---|---|---|---|---|---|---|---|---|---|
| | | | | 2 | 3 | 4 | 5 | 6 | 8 | 10 | 1/4 | 5/16 | 3/8 |
| | SOCKET HEAD CAP SCREW | 160,000 PSI | HIGH CARBON QUENCHED TEMPERED | | | | | | | | 16 (22) | 33 (45) | 54 (73) |
| | SOCKET SET SCREW | 212,000 PSI | HIGH CARBON QUENCHED TEMPERED | | | | | 9* | 16* | 30* | 70* | 140* | 18 (24) |
| | MACHINE SCREW STAINLESS | | 18-8 | 2.6* (294) | 4* (452) | 5.5* (622) | 8* (904) | 10* (1130) | 20* (2260) | 23* (2599) | 75* (8475) | 132* (14916) | 20 (27) |
| | MACHINE SCREW STAINLESS | | 316 | 2.7* (305) | 4* (452) | 5.7* (644) | 8* (904) | 10* (1130) | 22* (2486) | 25* (2825) | 80* (9040) | 140* (15820) | 22 (30) |
| | MACHINE SCREW YELLOW BRASS | 60,000 PSI | CU 63 ZN 37 | 2* (226) | 3.3* (3729) | 4.4* (497) | 6.4* (723) | 8* (904) | 16* (1808) | 20* (2260) | 65* (7345) | 110* (12430) | 17 (23) |
| | SILICONE BRONZE TYPE "B" | 70,000 PSI | CU 96 ZNI - 5 MIN | 2.3* (260) | 3.7* (418) | 4.9* (554) | 7.2* (814) | 10* (1130) | 19* (2147) | 22* (2486) | 70* (7910) | 125* (14125) | 20 (27) |
| | MACHINE SCREW ALUMINUM | 55,000 PSI | CU 3.8 - 4.9 1.2 - 1.8 MN .3 - .9 | 1.4* (158) | 2.1* (237) | 2.9* (328) | 4.3* (486) | 534* (610) | 12* (1356) | 15* (1695) | 46* (5198) | 82* (9266) | 13 (18) |
| | MACHINE SCREW MONEL | 82,000 PSI | NI 67 CU 30 FE 1.4 | 2.5* (283) | 4* (452) | 5.5* (622) | 8* (904) | 11* (1243) | 21* (2373) | 27* (3051) | 87* (9831) | 155* (17515) | 23 (31) |
| | SEM 5 HEAT TREATED STEEL | 120,000 PSI | 1018 1022 | 4* (452) | 5* (565) | 7* (791) | 11* (1243) | 15* (1695) | 27* (3051) | 37* (4181) | 90* (10170) | 200* (22600) | 330* (37290) |
| | STUDS | Use SAE 2, 5 and 8 values when grade is known, with nut of sufficient strength. | | | | | | | | | | | |
| | TAPPING SCREW | Set up joint as it will be in production. Use 70% of overtorque failure as production specifications. | | | | | | | | | | | |

| | | | | | | BODY SIZE OR OUTSIDE DIAMETER | | | | | | | | | | | | |
|---|---|---|---|---|---|---|---|---|---|---|---|---|---|---|---|---|---|---|
| 7/16 | 1/2 | 9/16 | 5/8 | 3/4 | 7/8 | 1 | 1-1/8 | 1-1/4 | 1-3/8 | 1-1/2 | 1-5/8 | 1-3/4 | 1-7/8 | 2 | 2-1/4 | 2-1/2 | 2-3/4 | 3 |
| 84 (114) | 125 (170) | 180 (244) | 250 (339) | 400 (542) | 640 (868) | 970 (1315) | 1520 (2061) | 2130 (2888) | 2850 (3865) | 3450 (4678) | 4700 (6373) | 6100 (8272) | 8200 (11119) | 8800 (11933) | 13000 (17628) | 18000 (24408) | 24000 (32544) | 31000 (42036) |
| 29 (39) | 43 (58) | 63 (85) | 100 (136) | 146 (198) | | | | | | | | | | | | | | |
| 31 (42) | 43 (58) | 58 (79) | 95 (129) | 130 (176) | 194 (263) | 260 (353) | 400 (542) | 500 (678) | | 725 (983) | | | | | | | | |
| 34 (46) | 46 (62) | 60 (81) | 100 (136) | 135 (183) | 210 (285) | 280 (380) | 425 (576) | 515 (698) | | 750 (1017) | | | | | | | | |
| 27 (37) | 37 (50) | 49 (66) | 78 (106) | 104 (141) | 160 (217) | 215 (292) | 325 (441) | 400 (542) | | 595 (807) | | | | | | | | |
| 30 (41) | 41 (56) | 53 (72) | 88 (119) | 117 (159) | 180 (244) | 250 (339) | 365 (495) | 450 (610) | | 655 (888) | | | | | | | | |
| 20 (27) | 27 (37) | 36 (49) | 62 (84) | 83 (113) | 128 (174) | 170 (231) | 255 (346) | 315 (427) | | 460 (624) | | | | | | | | |
| 36 (49) | 50 (68) | 67 (91) | 115 (156) | 155 (210) | 235 (319) | 315 (427) | 475 (644) | 585 (793) | | 850 (1153) | | | | | | | | |
| | | | | | | | | | | | | | | | | | | |

All figures are in foot-pounds (Newton-meters in parentheses) except those marked with an asterisk (*), which are inch-pounds (Newton-millimeters in parentheses). All of these values are for lubricated fasteners.

# Metric Fastener Torque Values

| Property Class and Head Markings | 4.8 | 8.8 | 9.8 | 10.9 | 12.9 |
|---|---|---|---|---|---|
| Property Class and Nut Markings | 5 | 10 | | 10 | 12 |

MIF (TS1163)

| | Class 4.8 | | | | Class 8.8 or 9.8 | | | | Class 10.9 | | | | Class 12.9 | | | |
|---|---|---|---|---|---|---|---|---|---|---|---|---|---|---|---|---|
| | Lubricated[a] | | Dry[a] | | Lubricated[a] | | Dry[a] | | Lubricated[a] | | Dry[a] | | Lubricated[a] | | Dry[a] | |
| SIZE | N•m | lb-ft | N•m | lb-ft | N•m | lb-ft | N•m | lb-ft | N•m | lb-ft | N•m | lb-ft | N•m | lb-ft | N•m | lb-ft |
| M6 | 4.8 | 3.5 | 6 | 4.5 | 9 | 6.5 | 11 | 8.5 | 13 | 9.5 | 17 | 12 | 15 | 11.5 | 19 | 14.5 |
| M8 | 12 | 8.5 | 15 | 11 | 22 | 16 | 28 | 20 | 32 | 24 | 40 | 30 | 37 | 28 | 47 | 35 |
| M10 | 23 | 17 | 29 | 21 | 43 | 32 | 55 | 40 | 63 | 47 | 80 | 60 | 75 | 55 | 95 | 70 |
| M12 | 40 | 29 | 50 | 37 | 75 | 55 | 95 | 70 | 110 | 80 | 140 | 105 | 130 | 95 | 165 | 120 |
| M14 | 63 | 47 | 80 | 60 | 120 | 88 | 150 | 110 | 175 | 130 | 225 | 165 | 205 | 150 | 260 | 109 |
| M16 | 100 | 73 | 125 | 92 | 190 | 140 | 240 | 175 | 275 | 200 | 350 | 225 | 320 | 240 | 400 | 300 |
| M18 | 135 | 100 | 175 | 125 | 260 | 195 | 330 | 250 | 375 | 275 | 475 | 350 | 440 | 325 | 560 | 410 |
| M20 | 190 | 140 | 240 | 180 | 375 | 275 | 475 | 350 | 530 | 400 | 675 | 500 | 625 | 460 | 800 | 580 |
| M22 | 260 | 190 | 330 | 250 | 510 | 375 | 650 | 475 | 725 | 540 | 925 | 675 | 850 | 625 | 1075 | 800 |
| M24 | 330 | 250 | 425 | 310 | 650 | 475 | 825 | 600 | 925 | 675 | 1150 | 850 | 1075 | 800 | 1350 | 1000 |
| M27 | 490 | 360 | 625 | 450 | 950 | 700 | 1200 | 875 | 1350 | 1000 | 1700 | 1250 | 1600 | 1150 | 2000 | 1500 |
| M30 | 675 | 490 | 850 | 625 | 1300 | 950 | 1650 | 1200 | 1850 | 1350 | 2300 | 1700 | 2150 | 1600 | 2700 | 2000 |
| M33 | 900 | 675 | 1150 | 850 | 1750 | 1300 | 2200 | 1650 | 2500 | 1850 | 3150 | 2350 | 2900 | 2150 | 3700 | 2750 |
| M36 | 1150 | 850 | 1450 | 1075 | 2250 | 1650 | 2850 | 2100 | 3200 | 2350 | 4050 | 3000 | 3750 | 2750 | 4750 | 3500 |

a. "Lubricated" means coated with a lubricant such as engine oil, or fasteners with phosphate and oil coatings. "Dry" means plain or zinc plated without any lubrication.

DO NOT use these hand torque values if a different torque value or tightening procedure is given for a specific application. Torque values listed are for general use only and include a ±10% variance factor. Check tightness of fasteners periodically. DO NOT use air powered wrenches.

Shear bolts are designed to fail under predetermined loads. Always replace shear bolts with identical grade.

Fasteners should be replaced with the same class. Make sure fastener threads are clean and that you properly start thread engagement. This will prevent them from failing when tightening.

When bolt and nut combination fasteners are used, torque values should be applied to the NUT instead of the bolt head.

Tighten plastic insert or crimped steel-type lock nuts to approximately 50 percent of the dry torque shown in the chart, applied to the nut, not to the bolt head. Tighten toothed or serrated-type lock nuts to the full torque value.

# Metric Fastener Torque Values – Grade 7

*NOTE: When bolting aluminum parts, tighten to 80% of torque specified in table.*

| Size | N•m | (lb-ft) |
|------|-----|---------|
| M6 | 9.5—12.2 | (7—9) |
| M8 | 20.3—27.1 | (15—20) |
| M10 | 47.5—54.2 | (35—40) |
| M12 | 81.4—94.9 | (60—70) |
| M14 | 128.8—146.4 | (95—108) |
| M16 | 210.2—240 | (155—177) |

# Inch Fastener Torque Values

| SAE Grade and Head Markings | No Marks (1 or 2[a]) | 5   5.1   5.2 | 8   8.2 |
|---|---|---|---|
| SAE Grade and Nut Markings | No Marks (2) | 5 | 8 |

MIF (TS1162)

| SIZE | Grade 1 | | | | Grade 2[a] | | | | Grade 5, 5.1 or 5.2 | | | | Grade 8 or 8.2 | | | |
|---|---|---|---|---|---|---|---|---|---|---|---|---|---|---|---|---|
| | Lubricated[b] | | Dry[b] | | Lubricated[b] | | Dry[b] | | Lubricated[b] | | Dry[b] | | Lubricated[b] | | Dry[b] | |
| | N•m | lb-ft | N•m | lb-ft | N•m | lb-ft | N•m | lb-ft | N•m | lb-ft | N•m | lb-ft | N•m | lb-ft | N•m | lb-ft |
| 1/4 | 3.7 | 2.8 | 4.7 | 3.5 | 6 | 4.5 | 7.5 | 5.5 | 9.5 | 7 | 12 | 9 | 13.5 | 10 | 17 | 12.5 |
| 5/16 | 7.7 | 5.5 | 10 | 7 | 12 | 9 | 15 | 11 | 20 | 15 | 25 | 18 | 28 | 21 | 35 | 26 |
| 3/8 | 14 | 10 | 17 | 13 | 22 | 16 | 27 | 20 | 35 | 26 | 44 | 33 | 50 | 36 | 63 | 46 |
| 7/16 | 22 | 16 | 28 | 20 | 35 | 26 | 44 | 32 | 55 | 41 | 70 | 52 | 80 | 58 | 100 | 75 |
| 1/2 | 33 | 25 | 42 | 31 | 53 | 39 | 67 | 50 | 85 | 63 | 110 | 80 | 120 | 90 | 150 | 115 |
| 9/16 | 48 | 36 | 60 | 45 | 75 | 56 | 95 | 70 | 125 | 90 | 155 | 115 | 175 | 130 | 225 | 160 |
| 5/8 | 67 | 50 | 85 | 62 | 105 | 78 | 135 | 100 | 170 | 125 | 215 | 160 | 215 | 160 | 300 | 225 |
| 3/4 | 120 | 87 | 150 | 110 | 190 | 140 | 240 | 175 | 300 | 225 | 375 | 280 | 425 | 310 | 550 | 400 |
| 7/8 | 190 | 140 | 240 | 175 | 190 | 140 | 240 | 175 | 490 | 360 | 625 | 450 | 700 | 500 | 875 | 650 |
| 1 | 290 | 210 | 360 | 270 | 290 | 210 | 360 | 270 | 725 | 540 | 925 | 675 | 1050 | 750 | 1300 | 975 |
| 1-1/8 | 470 | 300 | 510 | 375 | 470 | 300 | 510 | 375 | 900 | 675 | 1150 | 850 | 1450 | 1075 | 1850 | 1350 |
| 1-1/4 | 570 | 425 | 725 | 530 | 570 | 425 | 725 | 530 | 1300 | 950 | 1650 | 1200 | 2050 | 1500 | 2600 | 1950 |
| 1-3/8 | 750 | 550 | 950 | 700 | 750 | 550 | 950 | 700 | 1700 | 1250 | 2150 | 1550 | 2700 | 2000 | 3400 | 2550 |
| 1-1/2 | 1000 | 725 | 1250 | 925 | 990 | 725 | 1250 | 930 | 2250 | 1650 | 2850 | 2100 | 3600 | 2650 | 4550 | 3350 |

a. "Grade 2" applies for hex cap screws (not hex bolts) up to 152 mm (6 in.) long. "Grade 1" applies for hex cap screws over 152 mm (6 in.) long, and for all other types of bolts and screws of any length.

b. "Lubricated" means coated with a lubricant such as engine oil, or fasteners with phosphate and oil coatings. "Dry" means plain or zinc plated without any lubrication.

DO NOT use these hand torque values if a different torque value or tightening procedure is given for a specific application. Torque values listed are for general use only and include a ±10% variance factor. Check tightness of fasteners periodically. DO NOT use air powered wrenches.

Shear bolts are designed to fail under predetermined loads. Always replace shear bolts with identical grade.

Fasteners should be replaced with the same grade. Make sure fastener threads are clean and that you properly start thread engagement. This will prevent them from failing when tightening.

When bolt and nut combination fasteners are used, torque values should be applied to the NUT instead of the bolt head.

Tighten plastic insert or crimped steel-type lock nuts to approximately 50 percent of the dry torque shown in the chart, applied to the nut not to the bolt head. Tighten toothed or serrated-type lock nuts to the full torque value.

# ANSWERS TO TEST YOURSELF QUESTIONS

1. True. If enough of the hardened tip of the bit remains, the screwdriver can be reground and used again.

2. A soft hammer. Examples are lead, rawhide, plastic, brass, or rubber hammers.

3. False! Pliers are for holding work — not for loosening or tightening.

4. Pull — don't push. This will save your knuckles. (If you must push, use the base of your palm and keep your hand open.)

5. The offset allows more swing space in crowded places by "flopping" the wrench.

6. False. Adjustable wrenches should be placed on the nut so that the pulling force is applied only to the stationary jaw side of the wrench.

7. a. Torque—2 and 3; b. Tension—1 and 4.

8. 60 inch-pounds.

9. The bolt with a six-dash head is higher in strength.

10. Because heat caused by friction with the grinding wheel will draw out the temper in the metal and soften it until it is useless.

11. File only on the forward or pushing stroke. Raise the file from the work on the return stroke to prevent damage to the teeth.

12. Hacksaw teeth should point away from the handle.

13. At least two teeth should always contact the material being sawed.

14. External pullers, internal pullers, and press-pullers.

15. A knife-edge pulling attachment. This will reach in behind the whole bearing and prevent ruining it.

16. Two metals are joined using a third metal as an adhesive. Unlike welding, soldering does not involve melting the two metals to be joined.

17. The number "6" means 0.006, or six-thousandths of an inch.

18. False. The micrometer should never be tightened so that the work cannot be drawn from between the anvil and spindle.

19. Add readings as follows:

$$0.300$$
$$0.025$$
$$0.015$$
$$0.004$$

Total = 0.344 inch

20. "PSI" means "pound per square inch." This is a unit of measure for liquid or air pressure. "kPa" means kilopascal. This is the metric unit of measure for liquid or air pressure.

# INDEX